ORIENTAL

ORIENTAL
MYTHS AND LEGENDS

SENATE

Oriental – Myths & Legends

First published in 1889 as *Folklore and Legends – Oriental*
by W. W. Gibbings, London

This edition first published in 1996 by Senate, an imprint of
Random House UK Ltd, Random House, 20 Vauxhall Bridge
Road, London SW1V 2SA

ISBN 1 85958 199 4

Printed and bound in Guernsey by The Guernsey Press Co. Ltd

PREFATORY NOTE

The East is rich in Folklore, and the lorist is not troubled to discover material, but to select only that which it is best worth his while to preserve. The conditions under which the people live are most favourable to the preservation of the ancient legends, and the cultivation of the powers of narration fits the Oriental to present his stories in a more polished style than is usual in the Western countries. The reader of these tales will observe many points of similarity between them and the popular fictions of the West—similarity of thought and incident —and nothing, perhaps, speaks more eloquently the universal brotherhood of man than this

oneness of folk-fiction. At the same time, the
Tales of the East are unique, lighted up as they
are by a gorgeous extravagance of imagination
which never fails to attract and delight.

C. J. T.

CONTENTS

viii   CONTENTS.

THE COBBLER ASTROLOGER.

IN the great city of Isfahan lived Ahmed the obbler, an honest and industrious man, whose wish was to pass through life quietly; and he might have done so, had he not married a handsome wife, who, although she had condescended to accept of him as a husband, was far from being contented with his humble sphere of life.

Sittâra, such was the name of Ahmed's wife, was ever forming foolish schemes of riches and grandeur; and though Ahmed never encouraged them, he was too fond a husband to quarrel with what gave her pleasure. An incredulous smile or a shake of the head was his only answer to her often-told day-dreams; and she continued to persuade herself that she was certainly destined to great fortune.

It happened one evening, while in this temper of mind, that she went to the Hemmâm, where she saw a lady retiring dressed in a magnificent robe, covered with jewels, and surrounded by slaves. This was the very condition Sittâra had always

longed for, and she eagerly inquired the name of
the happy person who had so many attendants and
such fine jewels. She learned it was the wife of
the chief astrologer to the king. With this information she returned home. Her husband met her at
the door, but was received with a frown, nor could
all his caresses obtain a smile or a word; for several
hours she continued silent, and in apparent misery.
At length she said—

"Cease your caresses, unless you are ready to give
me a proof that you do really and sincerely love me."

"What proof of love," exclaimed poor Ahmed,
"can you desire which I will not give?"

"Give over cobbling; it is a vile, low trade, and
never yields more than ten or twelve dinars a day.
Turn astrologer! your fortune will be made, and I
shall have all I wish, and be happy."

"Astrologer!" cried Ahmed,—"astrologer! Have
you forgotten who I am—a cobbler, without any
learning—that you want me to engage in a profession which requires so much skill and knowledge?"

"I neither think nor care about your qualifica-
tions," said the enraged wife; "all I know is, that
if you do not turn astrologer immediately I will be
divorced from you to-morrow."

The cobbler remonstrated, but in vain. The
figure of the astrologer's wife, with her jewels and
her slaves, had taken complete possession of Sittâra's

imagination. All night it haunted her; she dreamt
of nothing else, and on awaking declared she would
leave the house if her husband did not comply with
her wishes. What could poor Ahmed do? He was
no astrologer, but he was dotingly fond of his wife,
and he could not bear the idea of losing her. He
promised to obey, and, having sold his little stock,
bought an astrolabe, an astronomical almanac, and
a table of the twelve signs of the zodiac. Furnished
with these he went to the market-place, crying, " I
am an astrologer! I know the sun, and the moon,
and the stars, and the twelve signs of the zodiac; I
can calculate nativities; I can foretell everything
that is to happen!"

No man was better known than Ahmed the
cobbler. A crowd soon gathered round him. "What!
friend Ahmed," said one, "have you worked till
your head is turned?" "Are you tired of looking
down at your last," cried another, "that you are
now looking up at the planets?" These and a
thousand other jokes assailed the ears of the poor
cobbler, who, notwithstanding, continued to exclaim
that he was an astrologer, having resolved on doing
what he could to please his beautiful wife.

It so happened that the king's jeweller was passing by. He was in great distress, having lost the
richest ruby belonging to the crown. Every search
had been made to recover this inestimable jewel,
but to no purpose; and as the jeweller knew he

could no longer conceal its loss from the king, he looked forward to death as inevitable. In this hopeless state, while wandering about the town, he reached the crowd around Ahmed and asked what was the matter. "Don't you know Ahmed the cobbler?" said one of the bystanders, laughing; "he has been inspired, and is become an astrologer."

A drowning man will catch at a broken reed: the jeweller no sooner heard the sound of the word astrologer, than he went up to Ahmed, told him what had happened, and said, "If you understand your art, you must be able to discover the king's ruby. Do so, and I will give you two hundred pieces of gold. But if you do not succeed within six hours, I will use all my influence at court to have you put to death as an impostor."

Poor Ahmed was thunderstruck. He stood long without being able to move or speak, reflecting on his misfortunes, and grieving, above all, that his wife, whom he so loved, had, by her envy and selfishness, brought him to such a fearful alternative. Full of these sad thoughts, he exclaimed aloud, "O woman, woman! thou art more baneful to the happiness of man than the poisonous dragon of the desert!"

The lost ruby had been secreted by the jeweller's wife, who, disquieted by those alarms which ever attend guilt, sent one of her female slaves to watch her husband. This slave, on seeing her master speak to the astrologer, drew near; and when she heard Ahmed, after some moments of apparent abstraction, compare a woman to a poisonous dragon, she was satisfied that he must know everything. She ran to her mistress, and, breathless with fear, cried, "You are discovered, my dear mistress, you are discovered by a vile astrologer. Before six hours are past the whole story will be known, and you will become infamous, if you are even so fortunate as to escape with life, unless you can find some way of prevailing on him to be merciful." She then related what she had seen and heard; and Ahmed's exclamation carried as complete conviction to the mind of the terrified mistress as it had done to that of her slave.

The jeweller's wife, hastily throwing on her veil, went in search of the dreaded astrologer. When she found him, she threw herself at his feet, crying, "Spare my honour and my life, and I will confess everything!"

"What can you have to confess to me?" exclaimed Ahmed in amazement.

"Oh, nothing! nothing with which you are not already acquainted. You know too well that I stole the ruby from the king's crown. I did so to punish my husband, who uses me most cruelly; and I thought by this means to obtain riches for myself, and to have him put to death. But you, most wonderful man, from whom nothing is hidden, have

discovered and defeated my wicked plan. I beg
only for mercy, and will do whatever you command
me."

An angel from heaven could not have brought
more consolation to Ahmed than did the jeweller's
wife. He assumed all the dignified solemnity that
became his new character, and said, "Woman! I
know all thou hast done, and it is fortunate for thee
that thou hast come to confess thy sin and beg for
mercy before it was too late. Return to thy house,
put the ruby under the pillow of the couch on
which thy husband sleeps; let it be laid on the
side furthest from the door; and be satisfied thy
guilt shall never be even suspected."

The jeweller's wife returned home, and did as she
was desired. In an hour Ahmed followed her, and
told the jeweller he had made his calculations, and
found by the aspect of the sun and moon, and by
the configuration of the stars, that the ruby was at
that moment lying under the pillow of his couch,
on the side furthest from the door. The jeweller
thought Ahmed must be crazy; but as a ray of
hope is like a ray from heaven to the wretched, he
ran to his couch, and there, to his joy and wonder,
found the ruby in the very place described. He
came back to Ahmed, embraced him, called him his
dearest friend and the preserver of his life, and gave
him the two hundred pieces of gold, declaring that
he was the first astrologer of the age.

These praises conveyed no joy to the poor cobbler, who returned home more thankful to God for his preservation than elated by his good fortune. The moment he entered the door his wife ran up to him and exclaimed, "Well, my dear astrologer! what success?"

"There!" said Ahmed, very gravely,—"there are two hundred pieces of gold. I hope you will be satisfied now, and not ask me again to hazard my life, as I have done this morning." He then related all that had passed. But the recital made a very different impression on the lady from what these occurrences had made on Ahmed. Sittâra saw nothing but the gold, which would enable her to vie with the chief astrologer's wife at the Hemmâm. "Courage!" she said, "courage! my dearest husband. This is only your first labour in your new and noble profession. Go on and prosper, and we shall become rich and happy."

In vain Ahmed remonstrated and represented the danger; she burst into tears, and accused him of not loving her, ending with her usual threat of insisting upon a divorce.

Ahmed's heart melted, and he agreed to make another trial. Accordingly, next morning he sallied forth with his astrolabe, his twelve signs of the zodiac, and his almanac, exclaiming, as before, "I am an astrologer! I know the sun, and the moon, and the stars, and the twelve signs of the zodiac; I

can calculate nativities; I can foretell everything
that is to happen!" A crowd again gathered round
him, but it was now with wonder, and not ridicule;
for the story of the ruby had gone abroad, and the
voice of fame had converted the poor cobbler Ahmed
into the ablest and most learned astrologer that was
ever seen at Isfahan.

While everybody was gazing at him, a lady passed
by veiled. She was the wife of one of the richest
merchants in the city, and had just been at the
Hemmâm, where she had lost a valuable necklace
and earrings. She was now returning home in great
alarm lest her husband should suspect her of having
given her jewels to a lover. Seeing the crowd
around Ahmed, she asked the reason of their assembling, and was informed of the whole story of the
famous astrologer : how he had been a cobbler, was
inspired with supernatural knowledge, and could,
with the help of his astrolabe, his twelve signs of
the zodiac, and his almanac, discover all that ever
did or ever would happen in the world. The story
of the jeweller and the king's ruby was then told
her, accompanied by a thousand wonderful circumstances which had never occurred. The lady, quite
satisfied of his skill, went up to Ahmed and mentioned her loss, saying : "A man of your knowledge
and penetration will easily discover my jewels; find
them, and I will give you fifty pieces of gold."

The poor cobbler was quite confounded, and looked

down, thinking only how to escape without a public exposure of his ignorance. The lady, in pressing through the crowd, had torn the lower part of her veil. Ahmed's downcast eyes noticed this; and wishing to inform her of it in a delicate manner, before it was observed by others, he whispered to her, "Lady, look down at the rent." The lady's head was full of her loss, and she was at that moment endeavouring to recollect how it could have occurred. Ahmed's speech brought it at once to her mind, and she exclaimed in delighted surprise : " Stay here a few moments, thou great astrologer. I will return immediately with the reward thou so well deservest." Saying this, she left him, and soon returned, carrying in one hand the necklace and earrings, and in the other a purse with the fifty pieces of gold. " There is gold for thee," she said, " thou wonderful man, to whom all the secrets of Nature are revealed ! I had quite forgotten where I laid the jewels, and without thee should never have found them. But when thou desiredst me to look at the rent below, I instantly recollected the rent near the bottom of the wall in the bathroom, where, before undressing, I had hid them. I can now go home in peace and comfort; and it is all owing to thee, thou wisest of men !"

After these words she walked away, and Ahmed returned to his home, thankful to Providence for his preservation, and fully resolved never again to tempt it. His handsome wife, however, could not yet rival the chief astrologer's lady in her appearance at the Hemmâm, so she renewed her entreaties and threats, to make her fond husband continue his career as an astrologer.

About this time it happened that the king's treasury was robbed of forty chests of gold and jewels, forming the greater part of the wealth of the kingdom. The high treasurer and other officers of state used all diligence to find the thieves, but in vain. The king sent for his astrologer, and declared that if the robbers were not detected by a stated time, he, as well as the principal ministers, should be put to death. Only one day of the short period given them remained. All their search had proved fruitless, and the chief astrologer, who had made his calculations and exhausted his art to no purpose, had quite resigned himself to his fate, when one of his friends advised him to send for the wonderful cobbler, who had become so famous for his extraordinary discoveries. Two slaves were immediately despatched for Ahmed, whom they commanded to go with them to their master. "You see the effects of your ambition," said the poor cobbler to his wife; "I am going to my death. The king's astrologer has heard of my presumption, and is determined to have me executed as an impostor."

On entering the palace of the chief astrologer, he was surprised to see that dignified person come forward to receive him, and lead him to the seat of honour, and not less so to hear himself thus addressed: "The ways of Heaven, most learned and excellent Ahmed, are unsearchable. The high are often cast down, and the low are lifted up. The whole world depends upon fate and fortune. It is my turn now to be depressed by fate; it is thine to be exalted by fortune."

His speech was here interrupted by a messenger from the king, who, having heard of the cobbler's fame, desired his attendance. Poor Ahmed now concluded that it was all over with him, and followed the king's messenger, praying to God that he would deliver him from this peril. When he came into the king's presence, he bent his body to the ground, and wished his majesty long life and prosperity. "Tell me, Ahmed," said the king, "who has stolen my treasure?"

"It was not one man," answered Ahmed, after some consideration; "there were forty thieves concerned in the robbery."

"Very well," said the king; "but who were they? and what have they done with my gold and jewels?"

"These questions," said Ahmed, "I cannot now answer; but I hope to satisfy your Majesty, if you will grant me forty days to make my calculations."

"I grant you forty days," said the king; "but when they are past, if my treasure is not found, your life shall pay the forfeit."

Ahmed returned to his house well pleased; for he resolved to take advantage of the time allowed him to fly from a city where his fame was likely to be his ruin.

"Well, Ahmed," said his wife, as he entered, "what news at Court?"

"No news at all," said he, "except that I am to be put to death at the end of forty days, unless I find forty chests of gold and jewels which have been stolen from the royal treasury."

"But you will discover the thieves."

"How? By what means am I to find them?"

"By the same art which discovered the ruby and the lady's necklace."

"The same art!" replied Ahmed. "Foolish woman! thou knowest that I have no art, and that I have only pretended to it for the sake of pleasing thee. But I have had sufficient skill to gain forty days, during which time we may easily escape to some other city; and with the money I now possess, and the aid of my former occupation, we may still obtain an honest livelihood."

"An honest livelihood!" repeated his lady, with scorn. "Will thy cobbling, thou mean, spiritless wretch, ever enable me to go to the Hemmâm like the wife of the chief astrologer? Hear me, Ahmed! Think only of discovering the king's treasure. Thou hast just as good a chance of doing so as thou hadst of finding the ruby, and the necklace and earrings.

At all events, I am determined thou shalt not
escape; and shouldst thou attempt to run away, I
will inform the king's officers, and have thee taken
up and put to death, even before the forty days are
expired. Thou knowest me too well, Ahmed, to
doubt my keeping my word. So take courage,
and endeavour to make thy fortune, and to place
me in that rank of life to which my beauty entitles
me."

The poor cobbler was dismayed at this speech;
but knowing there was no hope of changing his
wife's resolution, he resigned himself to his fate.
"Well," said he, "your will shall be obeyed. All I
desire is to pass the few remaining days of my life
as comfortably as I can. You know I am no scholar,
and have little skill in reckoning; so there are forty
dates: give me one of them every night after I have
said my prayers, that I may put them in a jar, and,
by counting them may always see how many of the
few days I have to live are gone."

The lady, pleased at carrying her point, took the
dates, and promised to be punctual in doing what
her husband desired.

Meanwhile the thieves who had stolen the king's
treasure, having been kept from leaving the city by
fear of detection and pursuit, had received accurate
information of every measure taken to discover
them. One of them was among the crowd before
the palace on the day the king sent for Ahmed;

and hearing that the cobbler had immediately
declared their exact number, he ran in a fright to
his comrades, and exclaimed, "We are all found
out! Ahmed, the new astrologer, has told the king
that there are forty of us."

"There needed no astrologer to tell that," said
the captain of the gang. "This Ahmed, with all
his simple good-nature, is a shrewd fellow. Forty
chests having been stolen, he naturally guessed that
there must be forty thieves, and he has made a
good hit, that is all; still it is prudent to watch
him, for he certainly has made some strange discoveries. One of us must go to-night, after dark, to
the terrace of this cobbler's house, and listen to his
conversation with his handsome wife; for he is said
to be very fond of her, and will, no doubt, tell her
what success he has had in his endeavours to detect
us."

Everybody approved of this scheme; and soon
after nightfall one of the thieves repaired to the
terrace. He arrived there just as the cobbler had
finished his evening prayers, and his wife was giving
him the first date. "Ah!" said Ahmed, as he took
it, "there is one of the forty."

The thief, hearing these words, hastened in con-
sternation to the gang, and told them that the
moment he took his post he had been perceived by
the supernatural knowledge of Ahmed, who immediately told his wife that one of them was there.

The spy's tale was not believed by his hardened companions; something was imputed to his fears; he might have been mistaken;—in short, it was determined to send two men the next night at the same hour. They reached the house just as Ahmed, having finished his prayers, had received the second date, and heard him exclaim, " My dear wife, to-night there are two of them ! "

The astonished thieves fled, and told their still incredulous comrades what they had heard. Three men were consequently sent the third night, four the fourth, and so on. Being afraid of venturing during the day, they always came as evening closed in, and just as Ahmed was receiving his date, hence they all in turn heard him say that which convinced them he was aware of their presence. On the last night they all went, and Ahmed exclaimed aloud, " The number is complete ! To-night the whole forty are here ! "

All doubts were now removed. It was impossible that Ahmed should have discovered them by any natural means. How could he ascertain their exact number ? and night after night, without ever once being mistaken ? He must have learnt it by his skill in astrology. Even the captain now yielded, in spite of his incredulity, and declared his opinion that it was hopeless to elude a man thus gifted ; he therefore advised that they should make a friend of the cobbler, by confessing everything to him,

and bribing him to secrecy by a share of the
booty.

His advice was approved of, and an hour before
dawn they knocked at Ahmed's door. The poor
man jumped out of bed, and supposing the soldiers
were come to lead him to execution, cried out,
"Have patience! I know what you are come for.
It is a very unjust and wicked deed."

"Most wonderful man!" said the captain, as the
door was opened, "we are fully convinced that thou
knowest why we are come, nor do we mean to
justify the action of which thou speakest. Here are
two thousand pieces of gold, which we will give
thee, provided thou wilt swear to say nothing more
about the matter."

"Say nothing about it!" said Ahmed. "Do you
think it possible I can suffer such gross wrong and
injustice without complaining, and making it known
to all the world?"

"Have mercy upon us!" exclaimed the thieves,
falling on their knees; "only spare our lives, and
we will restore the royal treasure."

The cobbler started, rubbed his eyes to see if he
were asleep or awake; and being satisfied that he
was awake, and that the men before him were really
the thieves, he assumed a solemn tone, and said:
"Guilty men! ye are persuaded that ye cannot
escape from my penetration, which reaches unto the
sun and moon, and knows the position and aspect of

every star in the heavens. Your timely repentance
has saved you. But ye must immediately restore
all that ye have stolen. Go straightway, and carry
the forty chests exactly as ye found them, and bury
them a foot deep under the southern wall of the old
ruined Hemmâm, beyond the king's palace. If ye
do this punctually, your lives are spared; but if ye
fail in the slightest degree, destruction will fall upon
you and your families."

The thieves promised obedience to his commands
and departed. Ahmed then fell on his knees, and
returned thanks to God for this signal mark of his
favour. About two hours after the royal guards
came, and desired Ahmed to follow them. He said
he would attend them as soon as he had taken leave
of his wife, to whom he determined not to impart
what had occurred until he saw the result. He bade
her farewell very affectionately; she supported herself with great fortitude on this trying occasion,
exhorting her husband to be of good cheer, and said
a few words about the goodness of Providence. But
the fact was, Sittâra fancied that if God took the
worthy cobbler to himself, her beauty might attract
some rich lover, who would enable her to go to the
Hemmâm with as much splendour as the astrologer's
lady, whose image, adorned with jewels and fine
clothes, and surrounded by slaves, still haunted her
imagination.

The decrees of Heaven are just: a reward suited

to their merits awaited Ahmed and his wife. The good man stood with a cheerful countenance before the king, who was impatient for his arrival, and immediately said, "Ahmed, thy looks are promising; hast thou discovered my treasure?"

"Does your Majesty require the thieves or the treasure? The stars will only grant one or the other," said Ahmed, looking at his table of astrological calculations. "Your Majesty must make your choice. I can deliver up either, but not both."

"I should be sorry not to punish the thieves," answered the king; "but if it must be so, I choose the treasure."

"And you give the thieves a full and free pardon?"

"I do, provided I find my treasure untouched."

"Then," said Ahmed, "if your majesty will follow me, the treasure shall be restored to you."

The king and all his nobles followed the cobbler to the ruins of the old Hemmâm. There, casting his eyes towards heaven, Ahmed muttered some sounds, which were supposed by the spectators to be magical conjurations, but which were in reality the prayers and thanksgivings of a sincere and pious heart to God for his wonderful deliverance. When his prayer was finished, he pointed to the southern wall, and requested that his majesty would order his attendants to dig there. The work was hardly begun, when the whole forty chests were found in the same state as when stolen, with the treasurer's seal upon them still unbroken.

The king's joy knew no bounds; he embraced Ahmed, and immediately appointed him his chief astrologer, assigned to him an apartment in the palace, and declared that he should marry his only daughter, as it was his duty to promote the man whom God had so singularly favoured, and had made instrumental in restoring the treasures of his kingdom. The young princess, who was more beautiful than the moon, was not dissatisfied with her father's choice; for her mind was stored with religion and virtue, and she had learnt to value beyond all earthly qualities that piety and learning which she believed Ahmed to possess. The royal will was carried into execution as soon as formed. The wheel of fortune had taken a complete turn. The morning had found Ahmed in a wretched hovel, rising from a sorry bed, in the expectation of losing his life; in the evening he was the lord of a rich palace, and married to the only daughter of a powerful king. But this change did not alter his character. As he had been meek and humble in adversity, he was modest and gentle in prosperity. Conscious of his own ignorance, he continued to ascribe his good fortune solely to the favour of Providence. He became daily more attached to the beautiful and

virtuous princess whom he had married; and he
could not help contrasting her character with that of
his former wife, whom he had ceased to love, and of
whose unreasonable and unfeeling vanity he was now
fully sensible.

THE LEGEND OF THE TERRESTRIAL
PARADISE OF SHEDDÁD,
THE SON OF 'A'D.

IT is related that 'Abd Allah, the son of Aboo Kilábeh, went forth to seek a camel that had run away, and while he was proceeding over the deserts of El-Yeman and the district of Seba, he chanced to arrive at a vast city encompassed by enormous fortifications, around the circuit of which were pavilions rising high into the sky. So when he approached it, he imagined that there must be inhabitants within it, of whom he might inquire for his camel; and, accordingly, he advanced, but on coming to it he found that it was desolate, without any one to cheer its solitude.

"I 'alighted," says he, "from my she-camel, and tied up her foot; and then, composing my mind, entered the city. On approaching the fortifications, I found that they had two enormous gates, the like of which, for size and height, have never been seen elsewhere in the world, set with a variety of jewels and jacinths, white and red, and yellow and green;

21

and when I beheld this, I was struck with the
utmost wonder at it, and the sight astonished me.
I entered the fortifications in a state of terror and
with a wandering mind, and saw them to be of the
same large extent as the city, and to comprise
elevated pavilions, every one of these containing
lofty chambers, and all of them constructed of gold
and silver, and adorned with rubies and chrysolites
and pearls and various-coloured jewels. The fold-
ing-doors of these pavilions were like those of the
fortifications in beauty, and the floors were overlaid
with large pearls, and with balls like hazel-nuts,
composed of musk and ambergris and saffron. And
when I came into the midst of the city, I saw not
in it a created being of the sons of Adam; and I
almost died of terror. I then looked down from
the summits of the lofty chambers and pavilions,
and saw rivers running beneath them; and in the
great thoroughfare-streets of the city were fruit-
bearing trees and tall palm-trees. And the construction of the city was of alternate bricks of gold and
silver; so I said within myself, No doubt this is the
paradise promised in the world to come.

"I carried away of the jewels which were as its
gravel, and the musk that was as its dust, as much
as I could bear, and returned to my district, where
I acquainted the people with the occurrence. And
the news reached Mo'áwiyeh, the son of Aboo
Sufyán (who was then Caliph), in the Hejáz; so he

wrote to his lieutenant in San'a of El-Yemen, saying, 'Summon that man, and inquire of him the
truth of the matter!' His lieutenant therefore
caused me to be brought, and demanded of me an
account of my adventure, and of what had befallen
me; and I informed him of what I had seen. He
then sent me to Mo'áwiyeh, and I acquainted him
also with that which I had seen, but he disbelieved
it; so I produced to him some of those pearls and
the little balls of ambergris and musk and saffron.
The latter retained somewhat of their sweet scent;
but the pearls had become yellow and discoloured.

"At the sight of these Mo'áwiyeh wondered, and
he sent and caused Kaab el-Ahbár to be brought
before him, and said to him, 'O Kaab el-Ahbár, I
have called thee on account of a matter of which I
desire to know the truth, and I hope that thou
mayest be able to certify me of it.' 'And what is
it, O Prince of the Faithful ?' asked Kaab el-Ahbár.
Mo'áwiyeh said, 'Hast thou any knowledge of the
existence of a city constructed of gold and silver,
the pillars whereof are of chrysolite and ruby, and
the gravel of which is of pearls, and of balls like
hazel-nuts, composed of musk and ambergris and
saffron?' He answered, 'Yes, O Prince of the
Faithful! It is Irem Zat-el-'Emád, the like of
which hath never been constructed in the regions of
the earth; and Sheddád, the son of 'A'd the Greater,
built it.' 'Relate to us,' said Mo'áwiyeh, 'some-

ORIENTAL FOLKLORE TALES.

thus :—

" ' 'A'd the Greater had two sons, Shedeed and
Sheddád, and when their father perished they
reigned conjointly over the countries after him, and
there was no one of the kings of the earth who was
not subject to them. And Shedeed the son of 'A'd
died, so his brother Sheddád ruled alone over the
earth after him. He was fond of reading the
ancient books; and when he met with the description of the world to come, and of paradise, with its
pavilions and lofty chambers, and its trees and
fruits, and of the other things in paradise, his heart
enticed him to construct its like on the earth, after
this manner which hath been above mentioned. He
had under his authority a hundred thousand kings,
under each of whom were a hundred thousand
valiant chieftains, and under each of these were a
hundred thousand soldiers. And he summoned them
all before him, and said to them, " I find in the
ancient books and histories the description of the
paradise that is in the other world, and I desire to
make its like upon the earth. Depart ye therefore
to the most pleasant and most spacious vacant tract
in the earth, and build for me in it a city of gold
and silver, and spread, as its gravel, chrysolites and
rubies and pearls, and as the supports of the vaulted
roofs of that city make columns of chrysolite, and
fill it with pavilions, and over the pavilions con-

struct lofty chambers, and beneath them plant, in the by-streets and great-thoroughfare streets, varieties of trees bearing different kinds of ripe fruits, and make rivers to run beneath them in channels of gold and silver." To this they all replied, "How can we accomplish that which thou hast described to us, and how can we procure the chrysolites and rubies and pearls that thou hast mentioned?" But he said, "Know ye not that the kings of the world are obedient to me, and under my authority, and that no one who is in it disobeyeth my command?" They answered, "Yes, we know that." "Depart then," said he, "to the mines of chrysolite and ruby, and to the places where pearls are found, and gold and silver, and take forth and collect their contents from the earth, and spare no exertions. Take also for me, from the hands of me, such of those things as ye find, and spare none, nor let any escape you; and beware of disobedience!"

" 'He then wrote a letter to each of the kings in the regions of the earth, commanding them to collect all the articles of the kinds above mentioned that their subjects possessed, and to repair to the mines in which these things were found, and extract the precious stones that they contained, even from the beds of the seas. And they collected the things that he required in the space of twenty years; after which he sent forth the geometricians and sages,

and labourers and artificers, from all the countries
and regions, and they dispersed themselves through
the deserts and wastes, and tracts and districts,
until they came to a desert wherein was a vast open
plain, clear from hills and mountains, and in it were
springs gushing forth, and rivers running. So they
said, "This is the kind of place which the king
commanded us to seek, and called us to find." They
then busied themselves in building the city according to the direction of the King Sheddád, king of
the whole earth, in its length and breadth; and
they made through it the channels for the rivers,
and laid the foundations conformably with the pre-
scribed extent. The kings of the various districts
of the earth sent thither the jewels and stones, and
large and small pearls, and carnelian and pure gold,
upon camels over the deserts and wastes, and sent
great ships with them over the seas; and a quantity
of those things, such as cannot be described nor
calculated nor defined, was brought to the workmen, who laboured in the construction of this city
three hundred years. And when they had finished
it, they came to the king and acquainted him with
the completion; and he said to them, "Depart, and
make around it impregnable fortifications of great
height, and construct around the circuit of the
fortifications a thousand pavilions, each with a
thousand pillars beneath it, in order that there may
be in each pavilion a vizier." So they went imme-

diately, and did this in twenty years; after which they presented themselves before Sheddád, and informed him of the accomplishment of his desire.

" ' He therefore ordered his viziers, who were a thousand in number, and his chief officers, and such of his troops and others as he confided in, to make themselves ready for departure, and to prepare themselves for removal to Irem Zat-el-'Emád, in attendance upon the king of the world, Sheddád, the son of 'A'd. He ordered also such as he chose of his women and his hareem, as his female slaves and his eunuchs, to fit themselves out. And they passed twenty years in equipping themselves. Then Sheddád proceeded with his troops, rejoiced at the accomplishment of his desire, until there remained between him and Irem Zat-el-'Emád one day's journey, when God sent down upon him and upon the obstinate infidels who accompanied him a loud cry from the heaven of His power, and it destroyed them all by the vehemence of its sound. Neither Sheddád nor any of those who were with him arrived at the city, or came in sight of it, and God obliterated the traces of the road that led to it, but the city remaineth as it was in its place until the hour of the judgment !'

" At this narrative, related by Kaab el-Ahbár, Mo'áwiyeh wondered, and he said to him, ' Can any one of mankind arrive at that city?' ' Yes,' answered Kaab el-Ahbár; ' a man of the companions of Mohammed (upon whom be blessing and peace!), in appearance like this man who is sitting here, without any doubt.' Esh-Shaabee also saith, 'It is related, on the authority of the learned men of Hemyer, in El-Yemen, that when Sheddád and those who were with him were destroyed by the loud cry, his son Sheddád the Less reigned after him; for his father, Sheddád the Greater, had left him as successor to his kingdom, in the land of Hadramót and Seba, on his departure with the troops who accompanied him to Irem Zat-el-'Emád. And as soon as the news reached him of the death of his father, on the way before his arrival at the city of Irem, he gave orders to carry his father's body from those desert tracts to Hadramót, and to excavate the sepulchre for him in a cavern. And when they had done this, he placed his body in it, upon a couch of gold, and covered the corpse with seventy robes, interwoven with gold and adorned with precious jewels; and he placed at his head a tablet of gold, whereon were inscribed these verses:—

> " 'Be admonished, O thou who art deceived by a pro-
> longed life!
> I am Sheddád, the son of 'A'd, the lord of a strong
> fortress,
> The lord of power and might, and of excessive valour.
> The inhabitants of the earth obeyed me, fearing my
> severity and threats;
> And I held the east and west under a strong dominion.
> And a preacher of the true religion invited us to the
> right way;

But we opposed him, and said, Is there no refuge from
it?

And a loud cry assaulted us from a tract of the distant
horizon ;

Whereupon we fell down like corn in the midst of a
plain at harvest ;

And now, beneath the earth, we await the threatened
day.'

" Eth-Tha'álibee also saith, ' It happened that two
men entered this cavern, and found at its upper end
some steps, and having descended these, they found
an excavation, the length whereof was a hundred
cubits, and its breadth forty cubits, and its height a
hundred cubits. And in the midst of this excavation was a couch of gold, upon which was a man of
enormous bulk, occupying its whole length and
breadth, covered with ornaments and with robes
interwoven with gold and silver; and at his head
was a tablet of gold, whereon was an inscription.
And they took that tablet, and carried away from
the place as much as they could of bars of gold and
silver and other things.' "

THE TOMB OF NOOSHEERWAN.

THE caliph Hâroon-oor-Rasheed went to visit the tomb of the celebrated Noosheerwân, the most famous of all the monarchs who ever governed Persia. Before the tomb was a curtain of gold cloth, which, when Hâroon touched it, fell to pieces. The walls of the tomb were covered with gold and jewels, whose splendour illumined its darkness. The body was placed in a sitting posture on a throne enchased with jewels, and had so much the appearance of life that, on the first impulse, the Commander of the Faithful bent to the ground, and saluted the remains of the just Noosheerwân.

Though the face of the departed monarch was like that of a living man, and the whole of the body in a state of preservation, which showed the admirable skill of those who embalmed it, yet when the caliph touched the garments they mouldered into dust. Hâroon upon this took his own rich robes and threw them over the corpse; he also hung up a new curtain richer than that he had destroyed, and perfumed the whole tomb with camphor, and other sweet scents.

It was remarked that no change was perceptible in the body of Noosheerwân, except that the ears had become white. The whole scene affected the caliph greatly; he burst into tears, and repeated from the Koran—"What I have seen is a warning to those who have eyes." He observed some writing upon the throne, which he ordered the Moobids (priests), who were learned in the Pehlevee language, to read and explain. They did so: it was as follows :—

"This world remains not; the man who thinks least of it is the wisest.

"Enjoy this world before thou becomest its prey.

"Bestow the same favour on those below thee as thou desirest to receive from those above thee.

"If thou shouldst conquer the whole world, death will at last conquer thee.

"Be careful that thou art not the dupe of thine own fortune.

"Thou shalt be paid exactly for what thou hast done; no more, no less."

The caliph observed a dark ruby-ring on the finger of Noosheerwân, on which was written—

"Avoid cruelty, study good, and never be precipitate in action.

"If thou shouldst live for a hundred years, never for one moment forget death.

"Value above all things the society of the wise."

Around the right arm of Noosheerwân was a clasp of gold, on which was engraved—

"On a certain year, on the 10th day of the month Erde-

behisht, a caliph of the race of Adean, professing the faith of
Mahomed, accompanied by four good men, and one bad,
shall visit my tomb."

Below this sentence were the names of the fore-
fathers of the caliph.   Another prophecy was added
concerning Hâroon's pilgrimage to Noosheerwân's
tomb.

"This prince will honour me, and do good unto me,
though I have no claim upon him ; and he will clothe me in
a new vest, and besprinkle my tomb with sweet-scented
essences, and then depart unto his home.   But the bad man
who accompanies him shall act treacherously towards me.
I pray that God may send one of my race to repay the great
favours of the caliph, and to take vengeance on his unworthy companion.   There is, under my throne, an inscription which the caliph must read and contemplate.   Its
contents will remind him of me, and make him pardon my
inability to give him more."

The caliph, on hearing this, put his hand under
the throne, and found the inscription, which con-
sisted of some lines, inscribed on a ruby as large as
the palm of the hand.   The Moobids read this also.
It contained information where would be found concealed a treasure of gold and arms, with some caskets
of rich jewels ; under this was written—

"These I give to the caliph in return for the good he has
done me ; let him take them and be happy."

When Hâroon-oor-Rasheed was about to leave the
tomb, Hoosein-ben-Sâhil, his vizier, said to him :
"O Lord of the Faithful, what is the use of all these

precious gems which ornament the abode of the
dead, and are of no benefit to the living? Allow
me to take some of them." The caliph replied with
indignation, "Such a wish is more worthy of a thief
than of a great or wise man." Hoosein was ashamed
of his speech, and said to the servant who had been
placed at the entrance of the tomb, "Go thou, and
worship the holy shrine within." The man went
into the tomb; he was above a hundred years old,
but he had never seen such a blaze of wealth. He
felt inclined to plunder some of it, but was at first
afraid; at last, summoning all his courage, he took
a ring from the finger of Noosheerwân, and came
away.

Hâroon saw this man come out, and observing
him alarmed, he at once conjectured what he had
been doing. Addressing those around him, he said,
"Do not you now see the extent of the knowledge
of Noosheerwân? He prophesied that there should
be one unworthy man with me. It is this fellow.
What have you taken?" said he, in an angry tone.
"Nothing," said the man. "Search him," said the
caliph. It was done, and the ring of Noosheerwân
was found. This the caliph immediately took, and,
entering the tomb, replaced it on the cold finger of
the deceased monarch. When he returned, a
terrible sound like that of loud thunder was heard.

Hâroon came down from the mountain on which
the tomb stood, and ordered the road to be made

inaccessible to future curiosity. He searched for, and found, in the place described, the gold, the arms, and the jewels bequeathed to him by Noosheerwân, and sent them to Bagdad.

Among the rich articles found was a golden crown, which had five sides, and was richly ornamented with precious stones. On every side a number of admirable lessons were written. The most remarkable were as follows :—

First side.

"Give my regards to those who know themselves.

"Consider the end before you begin, and before you advance provide a retreat.

"Give not unnecessary pain to any man, but study the happiness of all.

"Ground not your dignity upon your power to hurt others."

Second side.

"Take counsel before you commence any measure, and never trust its execution to the inexperienced.

"Sacrifice your property for your life, and your life for your religion.

"Spend your time in establishing a good name ; and if you desire fortune, learn contentment."

Third side.

"Grieve not for that which is broken, stolen, burnt, or lost.

"Never give orders in another man's house ; and accustom yourself to eat your bread at your own table.

"Make not yourself the captive of women."

Fourth side.

"Take not a wife from a bad family, and seat not thyself with those who have no shame.

"Keep thyself at a distance from those who are incorrigible in bad habits, and hold no intercourse with that man who is insensible to kindness.

"Covet not the goods of others.

"Be guarded with monarchs, for they are like fire which blazeth but destroyeth.

"Be sensible to your own value; estimate justly the worth of others; and war not with those who are far above thee in fortune."

Fifth side.

"Fear kings, women, and poets.

"Be envious of no man, and habituate not thyself to search after the faults of others.

"Make it a habit to be happy, and avoid being out of temper, or thy life will pass in misery.

"Respect and protect the females of thy family.

"Be not the slave of anger; and in thy contests always leave open the door of conciliation.

"Never let your expenses exceed your income.

"Plant a young tree, or you cannot expect to cut down an old one.

"Stretch your legs no further than the size of your carpet."

The caliph Hâroon-oor-Rasheed was more pleased with the admirable maxims inscribed on this crown than with all the treasures he had found. "Write these precepts," he exclaimed, "in a book, that the faithful may eat of the fruit of wisdom." When he returned to Bagdad, he related to his favourite vizier, Jaffier Bermekee, and his other chief officers, all that had passed; and the shade of Noosheerwân was propitiated by the disgrace of Hoosein-ben-Sâhil (who had recommended despoiling his tomb), and the exemplary punishment of the servant who had committed the sacrilegious act of taking the ring from the finger of the departed monarch.

AMEEN AND THE GHOOL.

THERE is a dreadful place in Persia called the "Valley of the Angel of Death." That terrific minister of God's wrath, according to tradition, has resting-places upon the earth and his favourite abodes. He is surrounded by ghools, horrid beings who, when he takes away life, feast upon the carcasses.

The natural shape of these monsters is terrible; but they can assume those of animals, such as cows or camels, or whatever they choose, often appearing to men as their relations or friends, and then they do not only transform their shapes, but their voices also are altered. The frightful screams and yells which are often heard amid these dreaded ravines are changed for the softest and most melodious notes. Unwary travellers, deluded by the appearance of friends, or captivated by the forms and charmed by the music of these demons, are allured from their path, and after feasting for a few hours on every luxury, are consigned to destruction.

The number of these ghools has greatly decreased

since the birth of the Prophet, and they have no power to hurt those who pronounce his name in sincerity of faith. These creatures are the very lowest of the supernatural world, and, besides being timid, are extremely stupid, and consequently often imposed upon by artful men.

The natives of Isfahan, though not brave, are the most crafty and acute people upon earth, and often supply the want of courage by their address. An inhabitant of that city was once compelled to travel alone at night through this dreadful valley. He was a man of ready wit, and fond of adventures, and, though no lion, had great confidence in his cunning, which had brought him through a hundred scrapes and perils that would have embarrassed or destroyed your simple man of valour.

This man, whose name was Ameen Beg, had heard many stories of the ghools of the "Valley of the Angel of Death," and thought it likely he might meet one. He prepared accordingly, by putting an egg and a lump of salt in his pocket. He had not gone far amidst the rocks, when he heard a voice crying, "Holloa, Ameen Beg Isfahânee! you are going the wrong road, you will lose yourself; come this way. I am your friend Kerreem Beg; I know your father, old Kerbela Beg, and the street in which you were born." Ameen knew well the power the ghools had of assuming the shape of any person they choose; and he also knew their skill as

genealogists, and their knowledge of towns as well
as families; he had therefore little doubt this was
one of those creatures alluring him to destruction.
He, however, determined to encounter him, and
trust to his art for his escape.

"Stop, my friend, till I come near you," was his
reply. When Ameen came close to the ghool, he
said, "You are not my friend Kerreem; you are a
lying demon, but you are just the being I desired to
meet. I have tried my strength against all the men
and all the beasts which exist in the natural world,
and I can find nothing that is a match for me. I
came therefore to this valley in the hope of en-
countering a ghool, that I might prove my prowess
upon him."

The ghool, astonished at being addressed in this
manner, looked keenly at him, and said, "Son of
Adam, you do not appear so strong." "Appear-
ances are deceitful," replied Ameen, "but I will
give you a proof of my strength. There," said he,
picking up a stone from a rivulet, "this contains a
fluid; try if you can so squeeze it that it will flow
out." The ghool took the stone, but, after a short
attempt, returned it, saying, "The thing is impossible." "Quite easy," said the Isfahânee, taking the
stone and placing it in the hand in which he had
before put the egg. "Look there!" And the
astonished ghool, while he heard what he took for
the breaking of the stone, saw the liquid run from

between Ameen's fingers, and this apparently without any effort.

Ameen, aided by the darkness, placed the stone upon the ground while he picked up another of a darker hue. "This," said he, "I can see contains salt, as you will find if you can crumble it between your fingers;" but the ghool, looking at it, confessed he had neither knowledge to discover its qualities nor strength to break it. "Give it me," said his companion impatiently; and, having put it into the same hand with the piece of salt, he instantly gave the latter all crushed to the ghool, who, seeing it reduced to powder, tasted it, and remained in stupid astonishment at the skill and strength of this wonderful man. Neither was he without alarm lest his strength should be exerted against himself, and he saw no safety in resorting to the shape of a beast, for Ameen had warned him that if he commenced any such unfair dealing, he would instantly slay him; for ghools, though long-lived, are not immortal.

Under such circumstances he thought his best plan was to conciliate the friendship of his new companion till he found an opportunity of destroying him.

"Most wonderful man," he said, "will you honour my abode with your presence? it is quite at hand: there you will find every refreshment; and after a comfortable night's rest you can resume your journey."

"I have no objection, friend ghool, to accept your offer; but, mark me, I am, in the first place, very passionate, and must not be provoked by any expressions which are in the least disrespectful; and, in the second, I am full of penetration, and can see through your designs as clearly as I saw into that hard stone in which I discovered salt. So take care you entertain none that are wicked, or you shall suffer."

The ghool declared that the ear of his guest should be pained by no expression to which it did not befit his dignity to listen; and he swore by the head of his liege lord, the Angel of Death, that he would faithfully respect the rights of hospitality and friendship.

Thus satisfied, Ameen followed the ghool through a number of crooked paths, rugged cliffs, and deep ravines, till they came to a large cave, which was dimly lighted. "Here," said the ghool, "I dwell, and here my friend will find all he can want for refreshment and repose." So saying, he led him to various apartments, in which were hoarded every species of grain, and all kinds of merchandise, plundered from travellers who had been deluded to this den, and of whose fate Ameen was too well informed by the bones over which he now and then stumbled, and by the putrid smell produced by some half-consumed carcasses.

"This will be sufficient for your supper, I hope,"

said the ghool, taking up a large bag of rice; "a man of your prowess must have a tolerable appetite." "True," said Ameen, "but I ate a sheep and as much rice as you have there before I proceeded on my journey. I am, consequently, not hungry, but will take a little lest I offend your hospitality." "I must boil it for you," said the demon; "you do not eat grain and meat raw, as we do. Here is a kettle," said he, taking up one lying amongst the plundered property. "I will go and get wood for a fire, while you fetch water with that," pointing to a bag made of the hides of six oxen.

Ameen waited till he saw his host leave the cave for the wood, and then with great difficulty he dragged the enormous bag to the bank of a dark stream, which issued from the rocks at the other end of the cavern, and, after being visible for a few yards, disappeared underground.

"How shall I," thought Ameen, "prevent my weakness being discovered? This bag I could hardly manage when empty; when full, it would require twenty strong men to carry it; what shall I do? I shall certainly be eaten up by this cannibal ghool, who is now only kept in order by the impression of my great strength." After some minutes' reflection the Isfahânee thought of a scheme, and began digging a small channel from the stream towards the place where his supper was preparing.

"What are you doing?" vociferated the ghool, as

he advanced towards him; "I sent you for water to boil a little rice, and you have been an hour about it. Cannot you fill the bag and bring it away?" "Certainly I can," said Ameen; "if I were content, after all your kindness, to show my gratitude merely by feats of brute strength, I could lift your stream if you had a bag large enough to hold it. But here," said he, pointing to the channel he had begun,— "here is the commencement of a work in which the mind of a man is employed to lessen the labour of his body. This canal, small as it may appear, will carry a stream to the other end of the cave, in which I will construct a dam that you can open and shut at pleasure, and thereby save yourself infinite trouble in fetching water. But pray let me alone till it is finished," and he began to dig. "Nonsense!" said the ghool, seizing the bag and filling it; "I will carry the water myself, and I advise you to leave off your canal, as you call it, and follow me, that you may eat your supper and go to sleep; you may finish this fine work, if you like it, to-morrow morning."

Ameen congratulated himself on this escape, and was not slow in taking the advice of his host. After having ate heartily of the supper that was prepared, he went to repose on a bed made of the richest coverlets and pillows, which were taken from one of the store-rooms of plundered goods. The ghool, whose bed was also in the cave, had no sooner laid down than he fell into a sound sleep. The anxiety of Ameen's mind prevented him from following his example; he rose gently, and having stuffed a long pillow into the middle of his bed, to make it appear as if he was still there, he retired to a concealed place in the cavern to watch the proceedings of the ghool. The latter awoke a short time before daylight, and rising, went, without making any noise, towards Ameen's bed, where, not observing the least stir, he was satisfied that his guest was in a deep sleep; so he took up one of his walking-sticks, which was in size like the trunk of a tree, and struck a terrible blow at what he supposed to be Ameen's head. He smiled not to hear a groan, thinking he had deprived him of life; but to make sure of his work, he repeated the blow seven times. He then returned to rest, but had hardly settled himself to sleep, when Ameen, who had crept into the bed, raised his head above the clothes and exclaimed, " Friend ghool, what insect could it be that has disturbed me by its tapping ? I counted the flap of its little wings seven times on the coverlet. These vermin are very annoying, for, though they cannot hurt a man, they disturb his rest ! "

The ghool's dismay on hearing Ameen speak at all was great, but that was increased to perfect fright when he heard him describe seven blows, any one of which would have felled an elephant, as seven flaps

AMEEN AND THE GHOOL.

of an insect's wing. There was no safety, he
thought, near so wonderful a man, and he soon
afterwards arose and fled from the cave, leaving the
Isfahânee its sole master.

When Ameen found his host gone, he was at no
loss to conjecture the cause, and immediately began
to survey the treasures with which he was surrounded, and to contrive means for removing them
to his home.

After examining the contents of the cave, and
arming himself with a matchlock, which had belonged
to some victim of the ghool, he proceeded to survey
the road. He had, however, only gone a short
distance when he saw the ghool returning with a
large club in his hand, and accompanied by a fox.
Ameen's knowledge of the cunning animal instantly
led him to suspect that it had undeceived his
enemy, but his presence of mind did not forsake
him. "Take that," said he to the fox, aiming a
ball at him from his matchlock, and shooting him
through the head,—"Take that for your not performing my orders. That brute," said he, "promised to
bring me seven ghools, that I might chain them, and
carry them to Isfahan, and here he has only brought
you, who are already my slave." So saying, he
advanced towards the ghool; but the latter had
already taken to flight, and by the aid of his club
bounded so rapidly over rocks and precipices that
he was soon out of sight.

Ameen having well marked the path from the cavern to the road, went to the nearest town and hired camels and mules to remove the property he had acquired. After making restitution to all who remained alive to prove their goods, he became, from what was unclaimed, a man of wealth, all of which was owing to that wit and art which ever overcome brute strength and courage.

THE RELATIONS OF SSIDI KUR.

GLORIFIED Nangasuna Garbi! thou art radiant within and without; the holy vessel of sublimity, the fathomer of concealed thoughts, the second of instructors, I bow before thee. What wonderful adventures fell to the lot of Nangasuna, and to the peaceful wandering Chan, and how instructive and learned the Ssidi will be found, all this is developed in thirteen pleasing narratives.

And I will first relate the origin of these tales :—

In the central kingdom of India there once lived seven brothers, who were magicians ; and one berren (a measure of distance) further dwelt two brothers, who were sons of a Chan. Now the eldest of these sons of the Chan betook himself to the magicians, that he might learn their art ; but although he studied under them for seven years, yet the magicians taught him not the true key to magic.

And once upon a time it happened that the youngest brother, going to bring food to the elder, peeped through the opening of the door, and obtained the key to magic. Thereupon, without delivering to the elder the food which he had brought for him, he returned home to the palace. Then said the younger son of the Chan to his brother, "That we have learned magic, let us keep to ourselves. We have in the stable a beautiful horse; take this horse, and ride not with him near the dwelling-place of the magicians, but sell the horse in their country, and bring back merchandise."

And when he had said thus, he changed himself into a horse. But the elder son of the Chan heeded not the words of his brother, but said unto himself: "Full seven years have I studied magic, and as yet have learned nothing. Where, then, has my young brother found so beautiful a horse? and how can I refuse to ride thereon?"

With these words he mounted, but the horse being impelled by the power of magic was not to be restrained, galloped away to the dwelling-place of the magicians, and could not be got from the door. "Well, then, I will sell the horse to the magicians." Thus thinking to himself, the elder called out to the magicians, "Saw ye ever a horse like unto this? My younger brother it was who found him." At these words the magicians communed with one another. "This is a magic horse; if magic grow at all common, there will be no wonderful art remaining. Let us, therefore, take this horse and slay him."

The magicians paid the price demanded for the horse, and tied him in a stall; and that he might not escape out of their hands, they fastened him, ready for slaughter, by the head, by the tail, and by the feet. "Ah!" thought the horse to himself, "my elder brother hearkened not unto me, and therefore am I fallen into such hands. What form shall I assume?" While the horse was thus considering, he saw a fish swim by him in the water, and immediately he changed himself into a fish.

But the seven magicians became seven herons, and pursued the fish, and were on the point of catching it, when it looked up and beheld a dove in the sky, and thereupon transformed itself into a dove. The seven magicians now became seven hawks, and followed the dove over mountains and rivers, and would certainly have seized upon it, but the dove, flying eastwards to the peaceful cave in the rock Gulumtschi, concealed itself in the bosom of Nangasuna Baktschi (the Instructor). Then the seven hawks became seven beggars, and drew nigh unto the rock Gulumtschi. "What may this import?" bethought the Baktschi to himself, "that this dove has fled hither pursued by seven hawks?" Thus thinking, the Baktschi said, "Wherefore, O dove, fliest thou hither in such alarm?" Then the dove related to him the cause of its flight, and spake afterwards as follows:—"At the entrance to the rock Gulumtschi stand seven beggars, and they will come to the Baktschi and say, ' We pray thee give us the rosary of the Baktschi ? ' Then will I transform myself into the Bumba of the rosary ; let the Baktschi then vouchsafe to take this Bumba into his mouth and to cast the rosary from him."

Hereupon the seven beggars drew nigh, and the Baktschi took the first bead into his mouth and the rest he cast from him. The beads which were cast away then became worms, and the seven beggars became fowls and ate up the worms. Then the Baktschi let the first bead fall from his mouth, and thereupon the first bead was transformed into a man with a sword in his hand. When the seven fowls were slain and become human corses, the Baktschi was troubled in his soul, and said these words, " Through my having preserved one single man have seven been slain. Of a verity this is not good."

To these words the other replied, " I am the Son of a Chan. Since, therefore, through the preservation of my life, several others have lost their lives, I will, to cleanse me from my sins, and also to reward the Baktschi, execute whatsoever he shall command me." The Baktschi replied thereto, " Now, then, in the cold Forest of Death there abides Ssidi Kur; the upper part of his body is decked with gold, the lower is of brass, his head is covered with silver. Seize him and hold him fast. Whosoever finds this

wonderful Ssidi Kur, him will I make for a thousand
years a man upon the earth."

Thus spake he, and the youth thereupon began
these words: "The way which I must take, the
food which I require, the means which I must
employ, all these vouchsafe to make known unto
me." To this the Baktschi replied, "It shall be as
thou demandest. At the distance of a berren (a
measure of distance) from this place you will come to
a gloomy forest, through which you will find there
runs only one narrow path. The place is full of
spirits. When thou reachest the spirits, they will
throng around you; then cry ye with a loud voice,
'Spirits, chu lu chu lu ssochi!' And when thou
hast spoken these words, they will all be scattered
like grain. When thou hast proceeded a little
further, you will encounter a crowd of other spirits;
then cry ye, 'Spirits, chu lu chu lu ssosi!' And a
little further on you will behold a crowd of child-
spirits: say unto these, 'Child-spirits, Ri ra pa
dra!' In the middle of this wood sits Ssidi Kur,
beside an amiri-tree. When he beholds you, he will
climb up it, but you must take the moon-axe, with
furious gestures draw nigh unto the tree, and bid
Ssidi Kur descend. To bring him away you will
require this sack, which would hold a hundred men.
To bind him fast this hundred fathoms of checkered
rope will serve you. This inexhaustible cake will
furnish thee with provender for thy journey. When

thou hast got thy load upon thy back, wander then
on without speaking, until thou art returned home
again. Thy name is Son of the Chan; and since
thou hast reached the peaceful rock Gulumtschi,
thou shalt be called the peaceful wandering Son of
the Chan."

Thus spake the Baktschi, and showed him the
way of expiation. When Ssidi Kur beheld his
pursuer, he speedily climbed up the amiri-tree, but
the Son of the Chan drew nigh unto the foot of the
tree, and spake with threatening words: "My
Baktschi is Nangasuna Garbi; mine axe is called
the white moon; an inexhaustible cake is my provender. This sack, capable of holding a hundred
men, will serve to carry thee away, this hundred
fathoms of rope will serve to bind thee fast; I myself am the peaceful wandering Son of the Chan.
Descend, or I will hew down the tree."

Then spake Ssidi Kur, "Do not hew down the
tree; I will descend from it."

And when he had descended, the Son of the Chan
thrust him into the sack, tied the sack fast with the
rope, ate of the butter-cake, and wandered forth
many days with his burden. At length Ssidi Kur
said to the Son of the Chan, "Since our long
journey is wearisome unto us, I will tell a story unto
you, or do you relate one unto me."

The Son of the Chan kept on his way, however,
without speaking a word, and Ssidi began afresh,

" If thou wilt tell a story, nod your head to me ; if I shall relate one, then do you shake your head."

But because the Son of the Chan shook his head from side to side, without uttering a word, Ssidi began the following tale :—

THE ADVENTURES OF THE RICH YOUTH.

" In former times there lived, in a great kingdom, a rich youth, a calculator, a mechanic, a painter, a physician, and a smith, and they all departed from their parents and went forth into a foreign land. When they at length arrived at the mouth of a great river, they planted, every one of them, a tree of life ; and each of them, following one of the sources of the river, set forth to seek their fortunes. 'Here,' said they to one another,—' here will we meet again. Should, however, any one of us be missing, and his tree of life be withered, we will search for him in the place whither he went to.'

" Thus they agreed, and separated one from another. And the rich youth found at the source of the stream, which he had followed, a pleasure-garden with a house, in the entrance to which were seated an old man and an old woman. 'Good youth,' exclaimed they both, 'whence comest thou — whither goest thou ?' The youth replied, 'I come from a distant country, and am going to seek my fortune.' And the old couple said unto him, 'It is

well thou hast come hither. We have a daughter,
slender of shape and pleasant of behaviour. Take
her, and be a son unto us!'

"And when they had so spoken, the daughter
made her appearance. And when the youth beheld
her, he thought unto himself, 'It is well I left my
father and my mother. This maiden is more beauteous than a daughter of the Tângâri (god-like spirits
of the male and female sex). I will take the maiden
and dwell here.' And the maiden said, 'Youth, it
is well that thou camest here.' Thereupon they
conversed together, went together into the house,
and lived peacefully and happily.

"Now, over the same country there reigned a
mighty Chan. And once in the spring-time, when
his servants went forth together to bathe, they
found, near the mouth of the river, in the water, a
pair of costly earrings, which belonged to the wife
of the rich youth. Because, therefore, these jewels
were so wondrously beautiful, they carried them to
the Chan, who, being greatly surprised thereat, said
unto his servants, 'Dwells there at the source of
the river a woman such as these belong to? Go,
and bring her unto me.'

"The servants went accordingly, beheld the
woman, and were amazed at the sight. 'This
woman,' said they to one another, 'one would never
tire of beholding.' But to the woman they said,
'Arise! and draw nigh with us unto the Chan.'

" Hereupon the rich youth conducted his wife to the presence of the Chan; but the Chan, when he beheld her, exclaimed, ' This maiden is a Tângâri, compared with her, my wives are but ugly.'

Thus spake he, and he was so smitten with love of her, that he would not let her depart from his house. But as she remained true and faithful to the rich youth, the Chan said unto his servants, ' Remove this rich youth instantly out of my sight.'

" At these commands the servants went forth, taking with them the rich youth, whom they led to the water, where they laid him in a pit by the side of the stream, covered him with a huge fragment of the rock, and thus slew him.

" At length it happened that the other wanderers returned from all sides, each to his tree of life ; and when the rich youth was missed, and they saw that his tree of life was withered, they sought him up the source of the river which he had followed, but found him not. Hereupon the reckoner discovered, by his calculations, that the rich youth was lying dead under a piece of the rock; but as they could by no means remove the stone, the smith took his hammer, smote the stone, and drew out the body. Then the physician mixed a life-inspiring draught, gave the same to the dead youth, and so restored him to life.

" They now demanded of him whom they had recalled to life, ' In what manner wert thou slain ?'

He accordingly related unto them the circumstances; and they communed one with another, saying, 'Let us snatch this extraordinary beautiful woman from the Chan!' Thereupon the mechanic constructed a wooden gerudin, or wonderful bird, which, when moved upwards from within, ascended into the air; when moved downwards, descended into the earth; when moved sideways, flew sideways accordingly. When this was done, they painted it with different colours, so that it was pleasant to behold.

"Then the rich youth seated himself within the wooden bird, flew through the air, and hovered over the roof of the royal mansion; and the Chan and his servants were astonished at the form of the bird, and said, 'A bird like unto this we never before saw or heard of.' And to his wife the Chan said, 'Go ye to the roof of the palace, and offer food of different kinds unto this strange bird.' When she went up to offer food, the bird descended, and the rich youth opened the door which was in the bird. Then said the wife of the Chan, full of joy, 'I had never hoped or thought to have seen thee again, yet now have I found thee once more. This has been accomplished by this wonderful bird.' After the youth had related to her all that had happened, he said unto her, 'Thou art now the wife of the Chan— but if your heart now yearns unto me, step thou into this wooden gerudin, and we will fly hence through the air, and for the future know care no more.'

"After these words the wife said, 'To the first husband to whom destiny united me am I inclined more than ever.' Having thus spoken they entered into the wooden gerudin, and ascended into the sky. The Chan beheld this, and said, 'Because I sent thee up that thou mightest feed this beautiful bird, thou hast betaken thyself to the skies.' Thus spake he full of anger, and threw himself weeping on the ground.

"The rich youth now turned the peg in the bird downwards, and descended upon the earth close to his companions. And when he stepped forth out of the bird, his companions asked him, 'Hast thou thoroughly accomplished all that thou didst desire?' Thereupon his wife also stepped forth, and all who beheld her became in love with her. 'You, my companions,' said the rich youth, 'have brought help unto me; you have awakened me from death; you have afforded me the means of once more finding my wife. Do not, I beseech you, rob me of my charmer once again.'

"Thus spake he; and the calculator began with these words :—'Had I not discovered by my calculation where thou wert lying, thou wouldst never have recovered thy wife.'

"'In vain,' said the smith, 'would the calculations have been, had I not drawn thee out of the rock. By means of the shattered rock it was that you obtained your wife. Then your wife belongs to me.'

"'A body,' said the physician, 'was drawn from out of the shattered rock. That this body was restored to life, and recovered his former wife, it was my skill accomplished it. I, therefore, should take the wife.'

"'But for the wooden bird,' said the mechanic, 'no one would ever have reached the wife. A numerous host attend upon the Chan; no one can approach the house wherein he resides. Through my wooden bird alone was the wife recovered. Let me, then, take her.'

"'The wife,' said the painter, 'never would have carried food to a wooden bird; therefore it was only through my skill in painting that she was recovered; I, therefore, claim her.'

"And when they had thus spoken, they drew their knives and slew one another."

"Alas! poor woman!" exclaimed the son of the Chan; and Ssidi said, "Ruler of Destiny, thou hast spoken words:—Ssarwala missbrod jackzang!" Thus spake he, and burst from the sack through the air.

Thus Ssidi's first tale treated of the adventures of the rich youth.

THE ADVENTURES OF THE BEGGAR'S SON.

When the Son of the Chan arrived as before at the cold Forest of Death, he exclaimed with threatening gestures at the foot of the amiri-tree, "Thou dead one, descend, or I will hew down the tree." Ssidi descended. The son of Chan placed him in the sack, bound the sack fast with the rope, ate of his provender, and journeyed forth with his burden. Then spake the dead one these words, "Since we have a long journey before us, do you relate a pleasant story by the way, or I will do so." But the Son of the Chan merely shook his head without speaking a word. Whereupon Ssidi commenced the following tale :—

"A long time ago there was a mighty Chan who was ruler over a country full of market-places. At the source of the river which ran through it there was an immense marsh, and in this marsh there dwelt two crocodile-frogs, who would not allow the water to run out of the marsh. And because there came no water over their fields, every year did both the good and the bad have cause to mourn, until such times as a man had been given to the frogs for the pests to devour. And at length the lot fell upon the Chan himself to be an offering to them, and needful as he was to the welfare of the kingdom, denial availed him not; therefore father and son communed sorrowfully together, saying, 'Which of us two shall go?'

"I am an old man," said the father, "and shall leave no one to lament me. I will go, therefore. Do you remain here, my son, and reign according as it is appointed."

"'O Tângâri,' exclaimed the son, 'verily this is not as it should be! Thou hast brought me up with care, O my father! If the Chan and the wife

of the Chan remain, what need is there of their son ?
I then will go, and be as a feast for the frogs.'

"Thus spake he, and the people walked sorrowfully round about him, and then betook themselves
back again. Now the son of the Chan had for his
companion the son of a poor man, and he went to
him and said, 'Walk ye according to the will of your
parents, and remain at home in peace and safety.
I am going, for the good of the kingdom, to serve
as a sacrifice to the frogs.'   At these words the son
of the poor man said, weeping and lamenting, 'From
my youth up, O Chan, thou hast carefully fostered
me.   I will go with thee, and share thy fate."

"Then they both arose and went unto the frogs ;
and on the verge of the marsh they heard the yellow
frog and the blue frog conversing with one another.
And the frogs said, 'If the son of the Chan and his
companion did but know that if they only smote off
our heads with the sword, and the son of the Chan
consumed me, the yellow frog, and the son of the
poor man consumed thee, the blue frog, they would
both cast out from their mouths gold and brass,
then would the country be no longer compelled to
find food for frogs.'

"Now, because the son of the Chan understood all
sorts of languages, he comprehended the discourse
of the frogs, and he and his companion smote the
heads of the frogs with their swords ; and when
they had devoured the frogs, they threw out from

their mouths gold and brass at their heart's pleasure. Then said the wanderers, 'The frogs are both slain —the course of the waters will be hemmed in no more. Let us then turn back unto our own country.' But the son of the Chan agreed not to this, and said, ' Let us not turn back into our own country, lest they say they are become spirits; therefore it is better that we journey further.'

" As they thereupon were walking over a mountain, they came to a tavern, in which dwelt two women, beautiful to behold—mother and daughter. Then said they, 'We would buy strong liquor that we might drink.' The women replied, ' What have ye to give in exchange for strong liquor ?' Thereupon each of them threw forth gold and brass, and the women found pleasure therein, admitted them into their dwelling, gave them liquor in abundance, until they became stupid and slept, took from them what they had, and then turned them out of doors.'

" Now when they awoke the son of the Chan and his companion travelled along a river and arrived in a wood, where they found some children quarrelling one with another. 'Wherefore,' inquired they, ' do you thus dispute ?'

" 'We have,' said the children, 'found a cap in this wood, and every one desires to possess it.'

" 'Of what use is the cap ?'

" 'The cap has this wonderful property, that whosoever places it on his head can be seen neither

by the Tângâri, nor by men, nor by the Tschadkurrs '
(evil spirits).

" ' Now go all of ye to the end of the forest and
run hither, and I will in the meanwhile keep the
cap, and give it to the first of you who reaches
me.'

" Thus spoke the son of the Chan ; and the children ran, but they found not the cap, for it was
upon the head of the Chan.   ' Even now it was
here,' said they, ' and now it is gone.'   And after
they had sought for it, but without finding it, they
went away weeping.

" And the son of the Chan and his companion
travelled onwards, and at last they came to a forest
in which they found a body of Tschadkurrs quarrelling one with another, and they said, ' Wherefore
do ye thus quarrel one with another ? '

" ' I,' exclaimed each of them, ' have made myself master of these boots.'

" ' Of what use are these boots ? ' inquired the
son of the Chan.

" ' He who wears these boots,' replied the Tschadkurrs, ' is conveyed to any country wherein he wishes
himself.'

" ' Now,' answered the son of the Chan, ' go all of
you that way, and he who first runs hither shall
obtain the boots.'

" And the Tschadkurrs, when they heard these
words, ran as they were told ; but the son of the Chan

had concealed the boots in the bosom of his companion, who had the cap upon his head. And the Tschadkurrs saw the boots no more; they sought them in vain, and went their way.

"And when they were gone, the prince and his companion drew on each of them one of the boots, and they wished themselves near the place of election in a Chan's kingdom. They wished their journey, laid themselves down to sleep, and on their awaking in the morning they found themselves in the hollow of a tree, right in the centre of the imperial place of election. It was, moreover, a day for the assembling of the people, to throw a Baling (a sacred figure of dough or paste) under the guidance of the Tângâri. 'Upon whose head even the Baling falls, he shall be our Chan.' Thus spake they as they threw it up; but the tree caught the Baling of Destiny. 'What means this?' exclaimed they all with one accord. 'Shall we have a tree for our Chan?'

"'Let us examine,' cried they one to another, 'whether the tree concealeth any stranger.' And when they approached the tree the son of the Chan and his companion stepped forth. But the people stood yet in doubt, and said one to another thus, 'Whosoever ruleth over the people of this land, this shall be decided to-morrow morning by what proceedeth from their mouths.' And when they had thus spoken, they all took their departure.

"On the following morning some drank water, and what they threw from their mouths was white; others ate grass, and what they threw from their mouths was green. In short, one threw one thing, and another another thing. But because the son of the Chan and his companion cast out from their mouths gold and brass, the people cried, 'Let the one be Chan of this people—let the other be his minister.' Thus were they nominated Chan and minister! And the daughter of the former Chan was appointed the wife of the new Chan.

"Now in the neighbourhood of the palace wherein the Chan dwelt was a lofty building, whither the wife of the Chan betook herself every day. 'Wherefore,' thought the minister, 'does the wife of the Chan betake herself to this spot every day?' Thus thinking, he placed the wonderful cap upon his head, and followed the Chan's wife through the open doors, up one step after another, up to the roof. Here the wife of the Chan gathered together silken coverlets and pillows, made ready various drinks and delicate meats, and burnt for their perfume tapers and frankincense. The minister being concealed by his cap, which made him invisible, seated himself by the side of the Chan's wife, and looked around on every side.

"Shortly afterwards a beautiful bird swept through the sky. The wife of the Chan received it with fragrance-giving tapers. The bird seated itself upon the roof and twittered with a pleasing voice; but out of the bird came Solangdu, the Son of the Tângâri, whose beauty was incomparable, and he laid himself on the silken coverlets and fed of the dainties prepared for him. Then spake the son of the Tângâri, 'Thou hast passed this morning with the husband whom thy fate has allotted to thee. What thinkest thou of him?' The wife of the Chan answered, 'I know too little of the prince to speak of his good qualities or his defects.' Thus passed the day, and the wife of the Chan returned home again.

"On the following day the minister followed the wife of the Chan as he had done before, and heard the son of the Tângâri say unto her, 'To-morrow I will come like a bird of Paradise to see thine husband.' And the wife of the Chan said, 'Be it so.'

"The day passed over, and the minister said to the Chan, 'In yonder palace lives Solangdu, the beauteous son of the Tângâri.' The minister then related all that he had witnessed, and said, 'To-morrow early the son of the Tângâri will seek thee, disguised like a bird of Paradise. I will seize the bird by the tail, and cast him into the fire; but you must smite him in pieces with the sword.'

"On the following morning, the Chan and the wife of the Chan were seated together, when the son of the Tângâri, transformed into a bird of

Paradise, appeared before them on the steps that led to the palace. The wife of the Chan greeted the bird with looks expressive of pleasure, but the minister, who had on his invisible-making cap, seized the bird suddenly by the tail, and cast him into the fire. And the Chan smote at him violently with his sword; but the wife of the Chan seized the hand of her husband, so that only the wings of the bird were scorched. 'Alas, poor bird!' exclaimed the wife of the Chan, as, half dead, it made its way, as well as it could, through the air.

"On the next morning the wife of the Chan went as usual to the lofty building, and this time, too, did the minister follow her. She collected together, as usual, the silken pillows, but waited longer than she was wont, and sat watching with staring eyes. At length the bird approached with a very slow flight, and came down from the bird-house covered with blood and wounds, and the wife of the Chan wept at the sight. 'Weep not,' said the son of the Tângâri; 'thine husband has a heavy hand. The fire has so scorched me that I can never come more.'

"Thus spoke he, and the wife of the Chan replied, 'Do not say so, but come as you are wont to do, at least come on the day of the full moon.' Then the son of the Tângâri flew up to the sky again, and the wife of the Chan began from that time to love her husband with her whole heart.

"Then the minister placed his wonderful cap
upon his head, and, drawing near to a pagoda, he
saw, through the crevice of the door, a man, who
spread out a figure of an ass, rolled himself over
and over upon the figure, thereupon took upon himself the form of an ass, and ran up and down bray-
ing like one.   Then he began rolling afresh, and
appeared in his human form.   At last he folded up
the paper, and placed it in the hand of a burchan
(a Calmuc idol).   And when the man came out the
minister went in, procured the paper, and remem-
bering the ill-treatment which he had formerly received, he went to the mother and daughter who
had sold him the strong liquor, and said, with
crafty words, 'I am come to you to reward you for
your good deeds.'   With these words he gave the
women three pieces of gold; and the women asked
him, saying, 'Thou art, indeed, an honest man, but
where did you procure so much gold?'   Then the
minister answered, 'By merely rolling backwards
and forwards over this paper did I procure this
gold.'   On hearing these words, the women said,
'Grant us that we too may roll upon it.'   And
they did so, and were changed into asses.   And the
minister brought the asses to the Chan, and the
Chan said, 'Let them be employed in carrying
stones and earth.'

"Thus spake he, and for three years were these
two asses compelled to carry stones and earth; and

their backs were sore wounded, and covered with bruises. Then saw the Chan their eyes filled with tears, and he said to the minister, 'Torment the poor brutes no longer.'

"Thereupon they rolled upon the paper, and after they had done so they were changed to two shrivelled women."

"Poor creatures!" exclaimed the Son of the Chan. Ssidi replied, "Ruler of Destiny, thou hast spoken words: Ssarwala missdood jakzank!" Thus spoke he, and flew out of the sack through the air.

And Ssidi's second relation treats of the adventures of the Poor Man's Son.

THE ADVENTURES OF MASSANG.

When the Son of the Chan arrived at the foot of the amiri-tree, and spoke as he had formerly done, Ssidi approached him, suffered himself to be placed in the sack, fastened with the rope, and carried away. Ssidi spoke as before, but the Son of the Chan shook his head, whereupon Ssidi began as follows :—

"A long time ago there lived in a certain country a poor man, who had nothing in the world but one cow ; and because there was no chance of the cow's calving, he was sore grieved, and said, 'If my cow does not have a calf, I shall have no more milk, and I must then die of hunger and thirst.'

"But when a certain number of moons had passed, instead of the calf the poor man had looked for he found a man with horns, and with a long tail like a cow. And at the sight of this monster the owner of the beast was filled with vexation, and he lifted up his staff to kill him; but the horned man said, 'Kill me not, father, and your mercy shall be rewarded.'

"And with these words he retreated into the depth of a forest, and there he found among the trees a man of sable hue. 'Who art thou?' inquired Massang the horned. 'I was born of the forest,' was the reply, 'and am called Iddar. I will follow thee whithersoever thou goest.'

"And they journeyed forth together, and at last they reached a thickly-covered grassy plain, and there they beheld a green man. 'Who art thou?' inquired they. 'I was born of the grass,' replied the green man, 'and will bear thee company.'

"Thereupon they all three journeyed forth together, until they came to a sedgy marsh, and there they found a white man. 'Who art thou?' inquired they. 'I was born of the sedges,' replied the white man, 'and will bear thee company.'

"Thereupon they all four journeyed forth together, until they reached a desert country, where, in the very depths of the mountain, they found a hut; and because they found plenty both to eat and to drink in the hut, they abode there. Every

day three of them went out hunting, and left the
fourth in charge of the hut.   On the first day,
Iddar, the Son of the Forest, remained in the hut,
and was busied preparing milk, and cooking meat
for his companions, when a little old woman put up
the ladder and came in at the door.   'Who's
there?' exclaimed Iddar, and, upon looking round,
he beheld an old woman about a span high, who
carried on her back a little sack.   'Oh, what, there
is somebody sitting there?' said the old woman,
'and you are cooking meat; let me, I beseech you,
taste a little milk and a little meat.'

"And though she merely tasted a little of each,
the whole of the food disappeared.   When the old
woman thereupon took her departure, the Son of
the Forest was ashamed that the food had disappeared, and he arose and looked out of the hut.
And as he chanced to perceive two hoofs of a horse,
he made with them a number of horse's footmarks
around the dwelling, and shot an arrow into the
court; and when the hunters returned home and
inquired of him, 'Where is the milk and the fatted
meat?' he answered them, saying, 'There came a
hundred horsemen, who pressed their way into the
house, and took the milk and the flesh, and they
have beaten me almost to death.   Go ye out, and
look around.'   And his companions went out when
they heard these words, looked around, saw the
prints of the horses' feet and the arrow which he

himself had shot, and said, 'The words which he spoke are true.'

"On the following day the Son of the Grass remained at home in the hut, and it befell him as it had befallen his companion on the previous day. But because he perceived the feet of two bullocks, he made with them the marks of the feet of many bullocks around the dwelling, and said to his companions, 'There came a hundred people with laden bullocks, and robbed me of the food I had prepared for you.'

"Thus spake he falsely. On the third day the Son of the Sedges remained at home in the hut, and because he met with no better fortune, he made, with a couple of the feet of a mule, a number of prints of mules' feet around the dwelling, and said to his companions, 'A hundred men with laden mules surrounded the house, and robbed me of the food I had prepared for you.'

"Thus spake he falsely. On the following day Massang remained at home in the hut, and as he was sitting preparing milk and flesh for his companions, the little old woman stepped in as before and said, 'Oh, so there is somebody here this time? Let me, I pray you, taste a little of the milk and a little of the meat.' At these words Massang considered, 'Of a certainty this old woman has been here before. If I do what she requires of me, how do I know that there will be any left?' And having thus considered, he said to the old woman, ' Old woman, before thou tastest food, fetch me some water.' Thus spoke he, giving her a bucket, of which the bottom was drilled full of holes, to fetch water in. When the old woman was gone, Massang looked after her, and found that the span-high old woman, reaching now up to the skies, drew the bucket full of water again and again, but that none of the water remained in it. While she was thus occupied, Massang peeped into the little sack which she carried on her shoulders, and took out of it a coil of rope, an iron hammer, and a pair of iron pincers, and put in their place some very rotten cords, a wooden hammer, and wooden pincers.

" He had scarcely done so before the old woman returned, saying, ' I cannot draw water in your bucket. If you will not give me a little of your food to taste, let us try our strength against each other.' Then the old woman drew forth the coil of rotten cords, and bound Massang with them, but Massang put forth his strength and burst the cords asunder. But when Massang had bound the old woman with her own coil, and deprived her of all power of motion, she said unto him, ' Herein thou hast gotten the victory ; now let us pinch each other with the pincers.'

" Whereupon Massang nipped hold of a piece of the old woman's flesh as big as one's head, and tore it forcibly from her. ' Indeed, youth,' cried the old

woman, sighing, 'but thou hast gotten a hand of
stone ; now let us hammer away at each other !'

"So saying, she smote Massang with the wooden
hammer on his breast, but the hammer flew from
the handle, and Massang was left without a wound.
Then drew Massang the iron hammer out of the
fire, and smote the old woman with it in such wise
that she fled from the hut crying and wounded.

"Shortly after this, the three companions returned
home, and said to Massang, 'Now, Massang, thou
hast surely had something to suffer?' But Massang
replied, 'Ye are all cowardly fellows, and have
uttered lies; I have paid off the old woman. Arise,
and let us follow her!'

"At these words they arose, followed her by
the traces of her blood, and at length reached a
gloomy pit in a rock. At the bottom of this pit
there were ten double circular pillars, and on the
ground lay the corpse of the old woman, among gold,
brass, and armour, and other costly things. 'Will
you three descend,' said Massang, 'and then pack
together the costly things, and I will draw them up,
or I will pack them, and you shall draw them out.'
But the three companions said, 'We will not go
down into the cavern, for of a verity the old woman
is a Schumnu' (a witch). But Massang, without
being dispirited, allowed himself to be let down
into the cavern, and collected the valuables, which
were then drawn forth by his companions. Then

his companions spoke with one another, saying, 'If
we draw forth Massang, he will surely take all these
treasures to himself. It were better, then, that we
should carry away these treasures, and leave Massang
behind in the cavern!'

"When Massang noticed that his three companions
treated him thus ungratefully, he looked about the
cavern in search of food, but between the pillars he
found nothing but some pieces of bark. Thereupon
Massang planted the bark in the earth, nourished
it as best he might, and said, 'If I am a true
Massang, then from this bark let there grow forth
three great trees. If I am not, then shall I die
here in this pit.'

"After these enchanting words, he laid himself
down, but from his having come in contact with the
corse of the old woman, he slept for many years.
When he awoke, he found three great trees which
reached to the mouth of the pit. Joyfully clambered
he up and betook himself to the hut, which was in
the neighbourhood. But, because there was no
longer any one to be found therein, he took his iron
bow and his arrows, and set forth in search of his
companions. These had built themselves houses
and taken wives. 'Where are your husbands?'
inquired Massang of their wives. 'Our husbands
are gone to the chase,' replied they. Then Massang
took arrow and bow, and set forth. His companions
were returning from the chase with venison, and

when they beheld Massang with arrow and bow, they cried, as with one accord, 'Thou art the well-skilled one! take thou our wives and property, we will now wander forth further!' At these words Massang said, 'Your behaviour was certainly not what it should have been; but I am going to reward my father—live on, therefore, as before.'

"By the way Massang discovered a brook, and out of the brook arose a beautiful maiden. The maiden went her way, and flowers arose out of her footsteps. Massang followed the maiden until he arrived in heaven, and when he was come there, Churmusta Tângâri (the Protector of the Earth) said unto him, 'It is well that thou art come hither, Massang. We have daily to fight with the host of Schumnu (witches). To-morrow look around; after to-morrow be companion unto us.'

" On the following day, when the white host were sore pressed by the black, Churmusta spake unto Massang : 'The white host are the host of the Tângâri, the black are the host of the Schumnu. To-day the Tângâri will be pressed by the Schumnu ; draw, therefore, thy bow, and send an arrow into the eye of the leader of the black host.' Then Massang aimed at the eye of the leader of the black host, and smote him, so that he fled with a mighty cry. Then spake Churmusta to Massang, " Thy deed is deserving of reward ; henceforward dwell with us for ever.' But Massang replied, 'I go to reward my father.'

"Hereupon Churmusta presented to Massang, Dschindamani, the wonder-stone of the Gods, and said unto him, 'By a narrow circuitous path you will reach the cave of the Schumnu. Go without fear or trembling therein. Knock at the door and say, "I am the human physician." They will then lead thee to the Schumnu Chan, that you may draw out the arrow from his eyes; then lay hands upon the arrow, scatter seven sorts of grain towards heaven, and drive the arrow yet deeper into his head.'

"Thus spake Churmusta authoritatively, and Massang obeyed his commands; reached, without erring, the cavern of the Schumnu, and knocked at the door. 'What hast thou learned?' inquired the woman. 'I am a physician,' answered Massang; and he was conducted into the building. He examined the wound of the Chan, and laid hands upon the arrow. 'Already,' said the Chan, 'my wound feels better.' But Massang suddenly drove the arrow further into the head, scattered the seven grains towards heaven, and a chain fell clattering from heaven down to earth.

"But while Massang was preparing to lay hands upon the chain, the Schumnu woman smote him with an iron hammer with such force, that from the blow there sprang forth seven stars."

"Then," said the Son of the Chan, "he was not able to reward his father."

"Ruler of Destiny, thou hast spoken words! Ssarwala missdood jonkzang." Thus spake Ssidi, and burst from the sack through the air.

Thus Ssidi's third relation treats of the adventures of Massang.

The Magician with the Swine's Head.

When the Son of the Chan had, as before, seized upon Ssidi, and was carrying him away, Ssidi spoke as formerly, but the Son of the Chan shook his head, without uttering a word, and Ssidi began the following relation :—

"A long while since there lived in a happy country a man and a woman. The man had many bad qualities, and cared for nothing but eating, drinking, and sleeping. At last his wife said unto him, 'By thy mode of life thou hast wasted all thine inheritance. Arise thée, then, from thy bed, and while I am in the fields, go you out and look about you!'

"As he, therefore, according to these words, was looking about him, he saw a multitude of people pass behind the pagoda with their herds; and birds, foxes, and dogs crowding and noising together around a particular spot. Thither he went, and there found a bladder of butter; so he took it home

and placed it upon the shelf. When his wife
returned and saw the bladder of butter upon the
shelf, she asked, 'Where found you this bladder of
butter?' To this he replied, 'I did according to
your word, and found this.' Then said the woman
'Thou went out but for an instant, and hast already
found thus much.'

"Then the man determined to display his
abilities, and said, 'Procure me then a horse, some
clothes, and a bloodhound.' The wife provided
them accordingly; and the man taking with him,
besides these, his bow, cap, and mantle, seated himself on horseback, led the hound in a leash, and rode
forth at random. After he had crossed over several
rivers he espied a fox. 'Ah,' thought he, 'that
would serve my wife for a cap.'

"So saying, he pursued the fox, and when it fled
into a hamster's hole, the man got off his horse,
placed his bow, arrows, and clothes upon the saddle,
fastened the bloodhound to the bridle, and covered
the mouth of the hole with his cap. The next
thing he did was to take a large stone, and hammer
over the hole with it; this frightened the fox, which
ran out and fled with the cap upon its head. The
hound followed the fox, and drew the horse along
with it, so that they both vanished in an instant,
and the man was left without any clothes.

After he had turned back a long way, he reached
the country of a mighty Chan, entered the Chan's

stable, and concealed himself in a stack of hay, so that merely his eyes were left uncovered. Not long afterwards, the beloved of the Chan was walking out, and wishing to look at a favourite horse, she approached close to the hayrick, placed the talisman of life of the Chan's kingdom upon the ground, left it there, and returned back to the palace without recollecting it. The man saw the wonderful stone, but was too lazy to pick it up. At sunset the cows came by, and the stone was beaten into the ground. Some time afterwards a servant came and cleansed the place, and the wonderful stone was cast aside upon a heap.

"On the following day the people were informed, by the beating of the kettledrums, that the beloved of the Chan had lost the wonderful stone. At the same time, all the magicians and soothsayers and interpreters of signs were summoned, and questioned upon the subject. On hearing this, the man in the hayrick crept out as far as his breast, and when the people thronged around him and asked, 'What hast thou learned?' he replied, 'I am a magician.' On hearing these words they exclaimed, 'Because the wondrous stone of the Chan is missing, all the magicians in the country are summoned to appear before him. Do you then draw nigh unto the Chan.' The man said, 'I have no clothes.' Hereupon the whole crowd hastened to the Chan, and announced unto him thus: 'In the hayrick there lieth a

magician who has no clothes. This magician would
draw nigh unto you, but he has nought to appear
in.' The Chan said, 'Send unto him this robe of
cloth, and let him approach.' It was done.

"The man was fetched, and after he had bowed
down to the Chan, he was asked what he needed
for the performance of his magic charms. To this
question he replied, 'For the performance of my
magic charms, it is needful that I should have the
head of a swine, some cloths of five colours, and
some baling' (a sacred figure of dough or paste).
When all these things were prepared, the magician
deposited the swine's head at the foot of a tree,
dressed it with the cloths of five colours, fastened
on the large baling, and passed the whole of three
nights in meditation. On the day appointed, all
the people assembled, and the magician having put
on a great durga (cloak), placed himself, with the
swine's head in his hand, in the street. When they
were all assembled together, the magician, showing
the swine's head, said, 'Here not and there not.'
All were gladdened at hearing these words. 'Because, therefore,' said the magician, 'the wonderful
stone is not to be found among the people, we must
seek for it elsewhere.'

"With these words the magician, still holding
the swine's head in his hand, drew nigh unto the
palace, and the Chan and his attendants followed
him, singing songs of rejoicing. When, at last, the

magician arrived at the heap, he stood suddenly
still, and exclaimed, 'There lies the wonderful
stone.'   Then, first removing some of the earth, he
drew forth the stone, and cleansed it.   'Thou art a
mighty magician,' joyfully exclaimed all who beheld
it.   'Thou art the master of magic with the swine's
head.   Lift up thyself that thou mayest receive thy
reward.'   The Chan said, 'Thy reward shall be
whatsoever thou wilt.'   The magician, who thought
only of the property he had lost, said, 'Give unto
me a horse, with saddle and bridle, a bow and
arrows, a cap, a mantle, a hound, and a fox.   Such
things give unto me.'   At these words the
Chan exclaimed, 'Give him all that he desireth.'
This was done, and the magician returned home
with all that he desired, and with two elephants,
one carrying meat, and the other butter.

" His wife met him close to his dwelling, with
brandy for him to drink, and said, ' Now, indeed,
thou art become a mighty man.'   Thereupon they
went into the house, and when they had laid themselves down to sleep, the wife said to him, ' Where
hast thou found so much flesh and so much butter ? '
Then her husband related to her circumstantially
the whole affair, and she answered him saying,
' Verily, thou art a stupid ass.   To-morrow I will
go with a letter to the Chan.'

" The wife accordingly wrote a letter, and in the
letter were the following words :—' Because it was

known unto me that the lost wondrous stone retained
some evil influence over the Chan, I have, for the
obviating of that influence, desired of him the dog
and the fox. What I may receive for my reward
depends upon the pleasure of the Chan.'

"The Chan read the letter through, and sent
costly presents to the magician. And the magician
lived pleasantly and happily.

"Now in a neighbouring country there dwelt
seven Chans, brethren. Once upon a time they
betook themselves, for pastime, to an extensive
forest, and there they discovered a beauteous maiden
with a buffalo, and they asked, 'What are you two
doing here? Whence come you?' The maiden
answered, 'I come from an eastern country, and am
the daughter of a Chan. This buffalo accompanies
me.' At these words these others replied, 'We are
the seven brethren of a Chan, and have no wife.
Wilt thou be our wife?'[1] The maiden answered,
'So be it.' But the maiden and the buffalo were
two Mangusch (a species of evil spirit like the
Schumnu), and were seeking out men whom they
might devour. The male Mangusch was a buffalo,
and the female, she who became wife to the
brethren.

"After the Mangusch had slain, yearly, one of
the brethren of the Chan, there was only one re-

---

[1] It is in accordance with the customs of Thibet for a
woman of that country to have several husbands.

maining. And because he was suffering from a grievous sickness, the ministers consulted together and said, 'For the sickness of the other Chans we have tried all means of cure, and yet have found no help, neither do we in this case know what to advise. But the magician with the swine's head dwells only two mountains off from us, and he is held in great estimation; let us, without further delay, send for him to our assistance.'

"Upon this four mounted messengers were despatched for the magician, and when they arrived at his dwelling, they made known to him the object of their mission. 'I will,' said the magician, 'consider of this matter in the course of the night, and will tell you in the morning what is to be done.'

"During the night he related to his wife what was required of him, and his wife said, 'You are looked upon, up to this time, as a magician of extraordinary skill; but from this time there is an end to your reputation. However, it cannot be helped, so go you must.'

"On the following morning the magician said to the messengers, 'During the night-time I have pondered upon this matter, and a good omen has presented itself to me in a dream. Let me not tarry any longer but ride forth to-day.' The magician, thereupon, equipped himself in a large cloak, bound his hair together on the crown of his head, carried in his left hand the rosary, and in his right the swine's head, enveloped in the cloths of five colours.

"When in this guise he presented himself before the dwelling-place of the Chan, the two Mangusch were sorely frightened, and thought to themselves, 'This man has quite the appearance, quite the countenance, of a man of learning.' Then the magician, first placing a baling on the pillow of the bed, lifted up the swine's head, and muttered certain magic words.

"The wife of the Chan seeing this discontinued tormenting the soul of the Chan, and fled in all haste out of the room. The Chan, by this conduct being freed from the pains of sickness, sank into a sound sleep. 'What is this?' exclaimed the magician, filled with affright. 'The disease has grown worse, the sick man uttereth not a sound; the sick man hath departed.' Thus thinking, he cried, 'Chan, Chan!' But because the Chan uttered no sound, the magician seized the swine's head, vanished through the door, and entered the treasure-chamber. No sooner had he done so, than 'Thief, thief!' sounded in his ears, and the magician fled into the kitchen; but the cry of 'Stop that thief! stop that thief!' still followed him. Thus pursued the magician thought to himself, 'This night it is of no use to think of getting away, so I will, therefore, conceal myself in a corner of the stable.' Thus thinking, he opened the door, and there found a buffalo, that lay there as if wearied with a long journey. The magician took the swine's head, and struck the buffalo three times between the horns, whereupon the buffalo sprang up and fled like the wind.

"But the magician followed after the buffalo, and when he approached the spot where he was, he heard the male Mangusch say to his female companion, 'Yonder magician knew that I was in the stable; with his frightful swine's head he struck me three blows—so that it was time for me to escape from him.' And the Chan's wife replied, 'I too am so afraid, because of his great knowledge, that I would not willingly return; for, of a certainty, things will go badly with us. To-morrow he will gather together the men with weapons and arms, and will say unto the women, "Bring hither firing;" when this is done he will say, "Lead the buffalo hither." And when thou appearest, he will say unto thee, "Put off the form thou hast assumed." And because all resistance would be useless, the people perceiving thy true shape will fall upon thee with swords, and spears, and stones; and when they have put thee to death, they will consume thee with fire. At last the magician will cause me to be dragged forth and consumed with fire. Oh, but I am sore afraid!'

"When the magician heard these words, he said to himself, 'After this fashion may the thing be easily accomplished.' Upon this he betook himself, with the swine's head to the Chan, lifted up the baling, murmured his words of magic, and asked, 'How is it now with the sickness of the Chan?' And the Chan replied, 'Upon the arrival of the master of magic the sickness passed away, and I have slept soundly.' Then the magician spake as follows : ' To-morrow, then, give this command to thy ministers, that they collect the whole of the people together, and that the women be desired to bring firing with them.'

"When, in obedience to these directions, there were two lofty piles of fagots gathered together, the magician said, 'Place my saddle upon the buffalo.' Then the magician rode upon the saddled buffalo three times around the assembled people, then removed the saddle from the buffalo, smote it three times with the swine's head, and said, ' Put off the form thou hast assumed.'

"At these words the buffalo was transformed into a fearful ugly Mangusch. His eyes were blood-shot, his upper tusks descended to his breast, his bottom tusks reached up to his eyelashes, so that he was fearful to behold. When the people had hewed this Mangusch to pieces with sword and with arrow, with spear and with stone, and his body was consumed upon one of the piles of fagots, then said the magician, 'Bring forth the wife of the Chan.' And with loud cries did the wife of the

Chan come forth, and the magician smote her with
the swine's head, and said, 'Appear in thine own
form!' Immediately her long tusks and bloodshot
eyes exhibited the terrific figure of a female Mangusch.

"After the wife of the Chan had been cut in
pieces, and consumed by fire, the magician mounted
his horse; but the people bowed themselves before
him, and strewed grain over him, presented him
with gifts, and regaled him so on every side, that
he was only enabled to reach the palace of the Chan
on the following morning. Then spake the Chan,
full of joy, to the magician, 'How can I reward you
for the great deed that thou hast done?' And the
magician answered, 'In our country there are but
few nose-sticks for oxen to be found. Give me, I
pray you, some of these nose-sticks.' Thus spake
he, and the Chan had him conducted home with
three sacks of nose-sticks, and seven elephants
bearing meat and butter.

"Near unto his dwelling his wife came with
brandy to meet him; and when she beheld the
elephants, she exclaimed, 'Now, indeed, thou art
become a mighty man.' Then they betook themselves to their house, and at night-time the wife of
the magician asked him, 'How camest thou to be
presented with such gifts?' The magician replied,
'I have cured the sickness of the Chan, and consumed with fire two Mangusch.' At these words

she replied, ‘Verily, thou hast behaved very fool-
ishly. After such a beneficial act, to desire nothing
but nose-sticks for cattle! To-morrow I myself
will go to the Chan.’

“On the morrow the wife drew near unto the
Chan, and presented unto him a letter from the
magician, and in this letter stood the following
words :—‘Because the magician was aware that of
the great evil of the Chan a lesser evil still remained behind, he desired of him the nose-sticks.
What he is to receive as a reward depends upon the
pleasure of the Chan.’

“‘He is right,’ replied the Chan, and he summoned the magician, with his father and mother,
and all his relations before him, and received them
with every demonstration of honour. ‘But for you
I should have died; the kingdom would have been
annihilated; the ministers and all the people consumed as the food of the Mangusch. I, therefore,
will honour thee,’ and he bestowed upon him proofs
of his favour.”

“Both man and wife were intelligent,” exclaimed
the Son of the Chan.

“Ruler of Destiny,” replied Ssidi, “thou hast
spoken words! Swarwala missdood jakzang!” Thus
spake he, and burst from the sack through the air.

Ssidi’s fourth relation treats of the Magician with
the head of the Swine.

The History of Sunshine and his Brother.

As the Chan's Son was journeying along as before,
laden with Ssidi, Ssidi inquired of him as formerly
who should tell a tale. But the Son of the Chan
shook his head without speaking a word, and Ssidi
began as follows :—

"Many years ago Guchanasschang reigned over
a certain happy land. This Chan had a wife and
a son, whose name was Sunshine (Narrani Garral).
Upon the death of his first wife the Chan married
a second; and by her likewise he had a son, and
the name of his second son was Moonshine (Ssarrani
Garral). And when both these sons were grown
up, the wife of the Chan thought to herself, 'So
long as Sunshine, the elder brother, lives, Moonshine,
the younger, will never be Chan over this land.'

"Some time after this the wife of the Chan fell
sick, and tossed and tumbled about on her bed from
the seeming agony she endured. And the Chan
inquired of her, 'What can be done for you, my
noble spouse?' To these words the wife of the
Chan replied, 'Even at the time I dwelt with my
parents I was subject to this sickness. But now it
is become past bearing. I know, indeed, but one
way of removing it; and that way is so impracti-
cable, that there is nothing left for me but to die.'
Hereupon spake the Chan, 'Tell unto me this way
of help, and though it should cost me half my

kingdom thou shalt have it. Tell me what thou requirest.' Thus spake he, and his wife replied with the following words, 'If the heart of one of the Chan's sons were roasted in the fat of the Gunsa (a beast); but thou wilt not, of course, sacrifice Sunshine for this purpose; and I myself bare Moonshine, his heart I will not consume. So that there is now nothing left for me but to die.' The Chan replied, ' Of a surety Sunshine is my son, and inexpressibly dear unto me; but in order that I may not lose thee, I will to-morrow deliver him over to the Jargatschi' (the servants of Justice).

" Moonshine overheard these words and hastened to his brother, and said, ' To-morrow they will murder thee.' When he had related all the circumstances, the brother replied, ' Since it is so, do you remain at home, honouring your father and mother. The time of my flight is come.' Then said Moonshine with a troubled heart, ' Alone I will not remain, but I will follow thee whithersoever thou goest.'

" Because the following day was appointed for the murder, the two brothers took a sack with baling-cakes from the altar, crept out at night, for it was the night of the full moon, from the palace, and journeyed on day and night through the mountainous country, until they at length arrived at the course of a dried-up river. Because their provender was finished, and the river afforded no water,

Moonshine fell to the earth utterly exhausted. Then spake the elder brother, full of affliction, 'I will go and seek water; but do you watch an instant until I come down from the high places.'

"After some vain attempts Sunshine returned, and found that his brother had departed this life. After he had with great tenderness covered the body of his brother with stones, he wandered over high mountains, and then arrived at the entrance of a cave. Within the cave sat an aged Arschi. 'Whence comest thou?' inquired the old man, 'thy countenance betokeneth deep affliction.' And when the youth had related all that had passed, the old man, taking with him the means of awakening the dead, went with the youth to the grave, and called Moonshine back to life. 'Will ye be unto me as sons?' Thus spake the old man, and the two young men became as sons unto him.

"Not far from this place there reigned a mighty Chan of fearful power; and the time was approaching in this country when the fields were watered, but the crocodiles prevented this. The crocodiles frequented a marsh at the source of the river, and would not allow the water to stream forth until such times as a Son of the Tiger-year[1] had been offered to them as food. After a time it happened

[1] Among the Calmucs every year has its peculiar name, and persons born in any year are called the children of that year.

that when search had been made in vain for a Son
of the Tiger-year, certain people drew nigh unto
the Chan, and said, 'Near unto the source of the
river dwelleth the old Arschi, and with him a Son
of the Tiger-year. Thither led we our cattle to
drink, and we saw him.'

"When he heard this, the Chan said, 'Go and
fetch him.'

"Accordingly the messengers were despatched for
him, and when they arrived at the entrance of the
cave, the Arschi himself came forth. 'What is it
that ye seek here?' inquired the aged Arschi.
'The Chan,' replied they, 'speaketh to thee thus:
Thou hast a Son of the Tiger-year. My kingdom
hath need of him: send him unto me.' But the
Arschi said, 'Who could have told you so? who,
indeed, would dwell with an old Arschi?'

"Thus speaking he retired into his cave, closed
the door after him, and concealed the youth in a
stone chest, placed the lid on him, and cemented
up the crevices with clay, as if it was from the dis-
tillation of arrack. But the messengers having
broken down the door, thrust themselves into the
cave, searched it, and then said, 'Since he whom we
sought is not here, we are determined that nothing
shall be left in the cave.' Thus speaking, they drew
their swords; and the youth said, out of fear for
the Arschi, 'Hurt not my father; I am here.'

"And when the youth was come forth, the mes-

sengers took him with them; but the Arschi they
left behind them weeping and sorrowing. When
the youth entered into the palace of the Chan, the
daughter of the Chan beheld him and loved him,
and encircled his neck with her arms. But the
attendants addressed the Chan, saying, 'To-day is
the day appointed for the casting of the Son of the
Tiger-year into the waters.' Upon this the Chan
said, 'Let him then be cast into the waters!' But
when they would have led him forth for that purpose, the daughter of the Chan spake and said,
'Cast him not into the waters, or cast me into the
waters with him.'

"And when the Chan heard these words, he was
angered, and said, 'Because this maiden careth so
little for the welfare of the kingdom, over which I
am Chan, let her be bound fast unto the Son of the
Tiger-year, and let them be cast together into the
waters.' And the attendants said, 'It shall be
according as you have commanded.'

"And when the youth was bound fast, and with
the maiden cast into the waters, he cried out, 'Since
I am the Son of the Tiger-year, it is certainly lawful
for them to cast me into the waters; but why
should this charming maiden die, who so loveth
me?' But the maiden said, 'Since I am but an
unworthy creature, it is certainly lawful for them
to cast me into the waters; but wherefore do they
cast in this beauteous youth?'

"Now the crocodiles heard these words, felt compassion, and placed the lovers once more upon the shore. And no sooner had this happened than the streams began to flow again. And when they were thus saved, the maiden said to the youth, 'Come with me, I pray you, unto the palace?' and he replied, 'When I have sought out my father Arschi, then will I come, and we will live together unsevered as man and wife.'

"Accordingly the youth returned to the cave of the old Arschi, and knocked at the door. 'I am thy son,' said he. 'My son,' replied the old man, 'has the Chan taken and slain; therefore it is that I sit here and weep.' At these words the son replied, 'Of a verity I am thy son. The Chan indeed bade them cast me into the waters; but because the crocodiles devoured me not, I am returned unto you. Weep not, O my father!'

"Arschi then opened the door, but he had suffered his beard and the hair of his head to grow, so that he looked like a dead man. Sunshine washed him therefore with milk and with water, and aroused him by tender words from his great sorrow.

"Now when the maiden returned back again to the palace, the Chan and the whole people were exceedingly amazed. 'The crocodiles,' they exclaimed, 'have, contrary to their wont, felt compassion for this maiden and spared her. This is

indeed a very wonder.' So the whole people passed
around the maiden, bowing themselves down before
her. But the Chan said, 'That the maiden is returned is indeed very good. But the Son of the
Tiger-year is assuredly devoured.' At these words
his daughter replied unto him, 'The Son of the
Tiger-year assuredly is not devoured. On account
of his goodness his life was spared him.'

"And when she said this, all were more than ever
surprised. 'Arise!' said the Chan to his ministers,
'lead this youth hither.' Agreeably to these commands, the ministers hastened to the cave of the
aged Arschi. Both Arschi and the youth arose, and
when they approached unto the dwelling of the
Chan, the Chan said, 'For the mighty benefits
which this youth has conferred upon us, and upon
our dominions, we feel ourselves bound to go forth
to meet him.'

"Thus spake he, and he went forth to meet the
youth, and led him into the interior of the palace,
and placed him upon one of the seats appropriated
to the nobles. 'O thou most wondrous youth!'
he exclaimed, 'art thou indeed the son of Arschi?'
The youth replied, 'I am the Son of a Chan. But
because my stepmother, out of the love she bare to
her own son, sought to slay me, I fled, and, accompanied by my younger brother, arrived at the cave
of the aged Arschi.'

"When the Son of the Chan related all this, the

Chan loaded him with honours, and gave his daughters for wives unto the two brothers, and sent them, with many costly gifts and a good retinue, home to their own kingdom. Thither they went, drew nigh unto the palace, and wrote a letter as follows :—' To the Chan their father, the two brothers are returned back again.'

"Now the father and mother had for many years bewailed the loss of both their sons, and their sorrows had rendered them so gloomy that they remained ever alone.

"On receipt of this letter they sent forth a large body of people to meet their children. But because the wife of the Chan saw both the youths approaching with costly gifts and a goodly retinue, so great was her envy that she died."

"She was very justly served!" exclaimed the Son of the Chan.

"Ruler of Destiny, thou hast spoken words! Ssarwala missdood jonkzang." Thus spake Ssidi, and burst from the sack through the air.

Thus Ssidi's fifth relation treats of Sunshine and his brother.

The Wonderful Man who overcame the Chan.

When the Son of the Chan had proceeded as formerly to seize the dead one, then spake he the

threatening words, seized upon Ssidi, thrust him
into the sack, tied the sack fast, ate of the butter-
cakes, and journeyed forth with his burden. After
Ssidi had as before asked who should tell the tale,
and the Son of the Chan had replied by merely shaking his head, Ssidi began the following relation :—

"A long, long time ago there lived in the land of
Barschiss, a wild, high-spirited man, who would not
allow any one to be above him. Then spake the
Chan of the kingdom to him, full of displeasure,
'Away with thee, thou good-for-nothing one ! Away
with thee to some other kingdom !' Thus spake he,
and the wild man departed forth out of the country.

"On his journey he arrived about mid-day at
a forest, where he found the body of a horse,
which had been somehow killed, and he accordingly
cut off its head, fastened it to his girdle, and climbed
up a tree.

"About midnight there assembled a host of
Tschadkurrs (evil spirits) mounted upon horses of
bark, wearing likewise caps of bark, and they placed
themselves around the tree. Afterwards there
assembled together other Tschadkurrs, mounted
upon horses of paper, and having caps of paper on
their heads, and they likewise placed themselves
around the tree.

"During the time that those who were assembled
were partaking of various choice wines and liquors,
the man peeped anxiously down from the tree, and

as he was doing so, the horse's head fell down from his belt. The Tschadkurrs were thereby exceedingly alarmed; so much that they fled hither and thither uttering fearful cries.

"On the following morning the man descended from the tree, and said, 'This night there was in this spot many choice viands and liquors, and now they are all vanished.' And while he was thus speaking, he found a brandy flask, and as he was anxious for something to drink, he immediately applied the flask which he had found to his lips; when suddenly there sprang out of it meat and cakes and other delicacies fit for eating. 'This flask,' cried he, 'is of a surety a wishing flask, which will procure him who has it everything he desires. I will take the flask with me.'

"And when he had thus spoken, he continued his journey until he met with a man holding a sword in his hand. 'Wherefore,' cried he, 'dost thou carry that sword in thine hand?' And the man answered, 'This sword is called Kreischwinger; and when I say to it, "Kreischwinger, thither goes a man who has taken such a thing from me, follow him and bring it back," Kreischwinger goes forth, kills the man, and brings my property back again.' To this the first replied, 'Out of this vessel springeth everything you desire; let us exchange.' So accordingly they made an exchange; and when the man went away with the flask, he who now owned the sword said, 'Kreischwinger, go forth now and bring me back my flask.'   So the sword went forth, smote his former master dead, and brought the golden vessel back again.

"When he had journeyed a little further, he met a man holding in his hand an iron hammer. 'Wherefore,' cried he, 'dost thou hold this hammer in thy hand ? ' To this question the other replied, 'When I strike the earth nine times with this hammer, there immediately arises a wall of iron, nine pillars high.' Then said the first, 'Let us make an exchange.' And when the exchange was made, he cried out, 'Kreischwinger, go forth and bring me back my golden vessel ! '

"After Kreischwinger had slain the man, and brought back the golden vessel, the man journeyed on until he encountered another man, carrying in his bosom a sack, made of goatskin, and he asked him, 'Wherefore keepest thou that sack ? ' To this question the other replied, 'This sack is a very wonderful thing. When you shake it, it rains heavily ; and if you shake it very hard, it rains very heavily.' Hereupon the owner of the flask said. 'Let us change,' and they changed accordingly ; and the sword went forth, slew the man, and returned back to its master with the golden vessel.

"When the man found himself in the possession of all these wonderful things, he said unto himself, 'The Chan of my country is indeed a cruel man ;

nevertheless I will turn back unto my native land.'
When he had thus considered, he turned back again,
and concealed himself in the neighbourhood of the
royal palace.

"About midnight he struck the earth nine times
with his iron hammer, and there arose an iron wall
nine pillars high.

"On the following morning the Chan arose, and
said, 'During the night I have heard a mighty tock,
tock at the back of the palace.' Thereupon the wife
of the Chan looked out, and said, 'At the back of
the palace there stands an iron wall nine pillars
high.' Thus spake she; and the Chan replied, full
of anger, 'The wild, high-spirited man has of a surety
erected this iron wall; but we shall see whether he
or I will be the conqueror.'

"When he had spoken these words the Chan
commanded all the people to take fuel and bellows,
and make the iron wall red-hot on every side.
Thereupon there was an immense fire kindled, and
the Wonderful Man found himself, with his mother,
within the wall of iron. He was himself upon the
upper pillars, but his mother was on the eighth.
And because the heat first reached the mother, she
exclaimed unto her son, 'The fires which the Chan
has commanded the people to kindle will destroy
the iron wall, and we shall both die.' The son
replied, 'Have no fear, mother, for I can find means
to prevent it.'

" When he had spoken these words he shook the
sack of goatskin, and there descended heavy rain
and extinguished the fire.   After that he shook the
sack still more forcibly, and there arose around
them a mighty sea, which carried away both the fuel
and the bellows which the people had collected."

"Thus, then, the Wonderful gained the mastery
over the Chan," exclaimed the Son of the Chan.

"Ruler of Destiny, thou hast spoken words !
Ssarwala missdood jakzang !"   Thus spake Ssidi,
and burst from the sack through the air.

Thus Ssidi's sixth relation treats of the Wonderful
Man who overpowered the Chan.

THE BIRD-MAN.

When the Son of the Chan had done as formerly,
spoken the threatening words, and carried off Ssidi,
Ssidi asked him as before to tell a tale ; but the
Son of the Chan shook his head without speaking
a word, and Ssidi began as follows :—

"In times gone by there lived in a fair country
the father of a family, whose three daughters had
daily by turns to watch over the calves.   Now it
once happened, during the time that the eldest
sister should have been watching the calves, that
she fell asleep, and one of them was lost.   When
the maiden awoke and missed the calf, she arose and
went forth to seek it, and wandered about until she
reached a large house with a red door.

"She went in, and then came to a golden door, next to that to a silver one, and last of all to a brazen door. After she had likewise opened this door she found, close to the entrance of it, a cage decorated with gold and all manner of costly jewels, and within it, on a perch, there stood a white bird.

"'I have lost a calf,' said the maiden, 'and am come hither to seek it.' At these words the bird said, 'If thou wilt become my wife I will find the calf for you, but not without.' But the maiden said, 'That may not be; among men birds are looked upon but as wild creatures. Therefore I will not become your wife, even though, through refusing, I lose the calf for ever.' And when she had thus spoken she returned home again.

"On the following day the second sister went forth to tend the calves, and she likewise lost one of them. And it happened unto her as it had done unto the eldest sister, and she too refused to become the wife of the bird.

"At last the youngest sister went forth with the calves, and when she missed one she too wandered on until she reached the house wherein the bird resided. The bird said unto her likewise, 'If thou wilt become my wife, I will procure for thee the calf which thou hast lost.' 'Be it according to thy will.' Thus spake she, and became the wife of the bird.

"After some time it happened that a mighty thirteen days' feast was held at a large pagoda in the neighbourhood, and upon this occasion a number of persons assembled together, amongst the rest the wife of the bird. And she was the foremost among the women; but among the men the most noticed was an armed man, who rode upon a white horse three times round the assemblage. And all who saw him exclaimed, 'He is the first.'

"And when the woman returned home again the white bird demanded of her, 'Who were the foremost among the men and the women who were there assembled together?' Then said the woman, 'The foremost among the men was seated upon a white horse, but I knew him not. The foremost of the women was myself.'

"And for eleven days did these things so fall out. But on the twelfth day, when the wife of the bird went to the assemblage, she sat herself down near an old woman. 'Who,' said the old woman, 'is the first in the assemblage this day?' To this question the wife of the bird replied, 'Among the men, the rider upon the white horse is beyond all comparison the foremost. Among the women, I myself am so. Would that I were bound unto this man, for my husband is numbered among wild creatures since he is nothing but a bird.'

"Thus spake she, weeping, and the old woman replied as follows :—'Speak ye no more words like unto these. Amongst the assembled women thou art in all things the foremost. But the rider upon the white horse is thine own husband. To-morrow is the thirteenth day of the feast. Come not to-morrow unto the feast, but remain at home behind the door until thine husband opens his birdhouse, takes his steed from the stable, and rides to the feast. Take ye, then, the open birdhouse and burn it. And when thou hast done this thy husband will remain henceforth and for ever in his true form.'

" The wife of the bird, thereupon, did as she had been told ; and when the birdhouse was opened, and her husband had departed, she took the birdhouse and burnt it upon the hearth. When the sun bowed down towards the west the bird returned home, and said to his wife, ' What, art thou already returned ? ' and she said, ' I am already returned.' Then said her husband, ' Where is my birdhouse ? ' And the wife replied, ' I have burnt it.' And he said, ' Barama, that is a pretty business—that bird-house was my soul.'

" And his wife was troubled, and said, ' What is now to be done ? ' To these words the bird replied, ' There is nothing can be done now, except you seat yourself behind the door, and there by day and night keep clattering a sword. But if the clatter-ing sword ceases, the Tschadkurrs will carry me away. Seven days and seven nights must ye thus defend me from the Tschadkurrs and from the Tângâri.'

" At these words the wife took the sword, propped

open her eyelids with little sticks, and watched for the space of six nights. On the seventh night her eyelids closed for an instant, but in that instant the Tschadkurrs and Tângâri suddenly snatched her husband away.

"Weeping bitterly, and despising all nourishment, the distracted wife ran about everywhere, crying unceasingly, 'Alas, my bird-husband! Alas, my bird-husband!'

"When she had sought for him day and night without finding him, she heard from the top of a mountain the voice of her husband. Following the sound, she discovered that the voice proceeded from the river. She ran to the river, and then discovered her husband with a load of tattered boots upon his back. 'Oh! my heart is greatly rejoiced,' said the husband, 'at seeing thee once more. I am forced to draw water for the Tschadkurrs and the Tângâri, and have worn out all these boots in doing so. If thou wishest to have me once again, build me a new birdhouse, and dedicate it to my soul; then I shall come back again.'

"With these words he vanished into the air. But the woman betook herself home to the house again, made a new birdhouse, and dedicated it to the soul of her husband. At length the bird-man appeared and perched himself on the roof of the house."

"Truly, his wife was an excellent wife!" exclaimed the Son of the Chan.

"Ruler of Destiny, thou hast spoken words! Ssarwala missdood jakzang!' Thus spake Ssidi, and burst from the sack through the air.

Thus Ssidi's seventh relation treats of the Bird-man.

THE PAINTER ND THE WOOD-CARVER.

When the Son of the Chan had, as on all the former occasions, spoken the words of threatening, placed the dead one in the sack, and journeyed forth with him, Ssidi spake this time also as follows :—
'The day is long, and the distant journey will tire us: do you relate a tale unto me, or I will relate one unto you." But the Son of the Chan shook his head without saying a word, and Ssidi began as follows :—

"Many years ago there lived in the land of Gujassmunn a Chan, whose name was Gunisschang. This Chan, however, died, and his son Chamuk Sakiktschi was elected Chan in his place. Now there lived among the people of that country a painter and a wood-carver, who bore similar names, and were evilly disposed towards each other.

"Once upon a time the painter, Gunga, drew nigh unto the Chan, and said unto him, ' Thy father hath been borne into the kingdom of the Tângâri, and hath said unto me, " Come unto me ! " Thither I went, and found thy father in great power and splendour; and I have brought for you this letter from him.' With these words the painter delivered unto the Chan a forged letter, the contents of which were as follows :—

"'This letter is addressed to my son Chamuk Sakiktschi.

"' When I departed this life, I was borne to the kingdom of the Tângâri. An abundance of all things reigns in this land; but since I am desirous of erecting a pagoda, and there are no wood-carvers to be found here, do you despatch unto me Cunga, the wood-carver. The means by which he is to reach this place he may learn from the painter.'

" After he had perused this letter, the Chan of Gujassmunn said, 'If my father has really been carried into the realms of the Tângâri, that would indeed be a good thing. Call hither the wood-carver ?' The wood-carver was called, and appeared before the Chan, and the Chan said unto him, ' My father has been carried into the realms of the Tângâri. He is desirous of erecting a pagoda, and because there are no wood-carvers there he is desirous that you should be despatched unto him.'

" With these words the Chan displayed the forged letter, and when he had read it, the wood-carver said unto himself, ' Of a surety Gunga, the painter, has played me this trick; but I will try if I cannot overreach him.'

" Thus thinking, he inquired of the painter, ' By

what means can I reach the kingdom of the Tângâri ?'

" To these words the painter replied, 'When thou hast prepared all thy tools and implements of trade, then place thyself upon a pile of fagots, and when thou hast sung songs of rejoicing and set light to the pile of fagots, thus wilt thou be able to reach the kingdom of the Tângâri.' Thus spake he, and the seventh night from that time was appointed for the carver's setting forth on his journey.

" When the wood-carver returned home unto his wife, he spake unto her these words :—' The painter hath conceived wickedness in his mind against me; yet I shall try means to overreach him.'

" Accordingly he secretly contrived a subterranean passage, which reached from his own house into the middle of his field. Over the aperture in the field he placed a large stone, covered the stone with earth, and when the seventh night was come, the Chan said, 'This night let the wood-carver draw nigh unto the Chan, my father.' Thereupon, agreeably to the commands of the Chan, every one of the people brought out a handful of the fat of the Gunsa (a beast). A huge fire was kindled, and the wood-cutter, when he had sung the songs of rejoicing, escaped by the covered way he had made back to his own house.

" Meanwhile the painter was greatly rejoiced, and pointed upwards with his finger, and said, 'There

rideth the wood-carver up to heaven.' All who had
been present, too, betook themselves home, thinking
in their hearts, 'The wood-carver is dead, and gone
up above to the Chan.'

"The wood-carver remained concealed at home
a whole month, and allowed no man to set eyes
upon him, but washed his head in milk every day,
and kept himself always in the shade. After that
he put on a garment of white silk, and wrote a
letter, in which stood the following words:—

"'This letter is addressed to my son Chamuk
Sakiktschi. That thou rulest the kingdom in
peace; it is very good. Since thy wood-carver has
completed his work, it is needful that he should be
rewarded according to his deserts. Since, moreover, for the decoration of the pagoda, many
coloured paintings are necessary, send unto me the
painter, as thou hast already sent this man.'

"The wood-carver then drew nigh unto the Chan
with this letter. 'What!' cried the Chan, 'art
thou returned from the kingdom of the Tângâri?'
The wood-carver handed the letter unto him, and
said, 'I have, indeed, been in the kingdom of the
Tângâri, and from it I am returned home again.'

"The Chan was greatly rejoiced when he heard
this, and rewarded the wood-carver with costly
presents. 'Because the painter is now required,'
said the Chan, 'for the painting of the pagoda, let
him now be called before me.'

"The painter drew nigh accordingly, and when he saw the wood-carver, fair, and in white-shining robes, and decorated with gifts, he said unto himself, 'Then he is not dead!' And the Chan handed over to the painter the forged letter, with the seal thereto, and said, 'Thou must go now.'

"And when the seventh night from that time arrived, the people came forward as before with a contribution of the fat of the Gunsa; and in the midst of the field a pile of fagots was kindled. The painter seated himself in the midst of the fire, with his materials for painting, and a letter and gifts of honour for the Chan Gunisschang, and sang songs of rejoicing; and as the fire kept growing more and more intolerable, he lifted up his voice and uttered piercing cries; but the noise of the instruments overpowered his voice, and at length the fire consumed him."

"He was properly rewarded!" exclaimed the Son of the Chan.

"Ruler of Destiny, thou hast spoken words! Ssarwala missdood jakzang!" Thus spake Ssidi, and burst from the sack through the air.

Thus Ssidi's eighth relation treats of the Painter and the Wood-carver.

THE STEALING OF THE HEART.

When the Son of the Chan was, as formerly, carrying Ssidi away in the sack, Ssidi inquired of him as before; but the Son of the Chan shook his head without speaking a word, so Ssidi proceeded as follows :—

"Many, many years ago there ruled over a certain kingdom a Chan named Guguluktschi. Upon the death of this Chan his son, who was of great reputation and worth, was elected Chan in his place.

"One berren (a measure of distance) from the residence of the Chan dwelt a man, who had a daughter of wonderful abilities and extraordinary beauty. The son of the Chan was enamoured of this maiden, and visited her daily; until, at length, he fell sick of a grievous malady, and died, without the maiden being made aware of it.

"One night, just as the moon was rising, the maiden heard a knocking at the door, and the face of the maiden was gladdened when she beheld the son of the Chan; and the maiden arose and went to meet him, and she led him in and placed arrack and cakes before him. 'Wife,' said the son of the Chan, 'come with me!'

"The maiden followed, and they kept going further and further, until they arrived at the dwelling of the Chan, from which proceeded the sound of cymbals and kettledrums.

"'Chan, what is this?' she asked. The son of the Chan replied to these inquiries of the maiden, 'Do you not know that they are now celebrating the feast of my funeral?' Thus spake he; and the maiden replied, 'The feast of thy funeral! Has anything then befallen the Chan's son?' And the son of the Chan replied, 'He is departed. Thou wilt, however, bear a son unto him. And when the season is come, go into the stable of the elephant, and let him be born there. In the palace there will arise a contention betwixt my mother and her attendants, because of the wonderful stone of the kingdom. The wonderful stone lies under the table of sacrifice. After it has been discovered, do you and my mother reign over this kingdom until such time as my son comes of age.'

"Thus spake he, and vanished into air. But his beloved fell, from very anguish, into a swoon. 'Chan! Chan!' exclaimed she sorrowfully, when she came to herself again. And because she felt that the time was come, she betook herself to the stable of the elephants, and there gave birth to a son.

"On the following morning, when the keeper of the elephants entered the stable, he exclaimed, 'What! has a woman given birth to a son in the stable of the elephants? This never happened before. This may be an injury to the elephants.'

"At these words the maiden said, 'Go unto the mother of the Chan, and say unto her, "Arise! something wonderful has taken place."'

"When these words were told unto the mother of the Chan, then she arose and went unto the stable,

and the maiden related unto her all that had
happened. 'Wonderful!' said the mother of the
Chan. 'Otherwise the Chan had left no successors.
Let us go together into the house.'

"Thus speaking, she took the maiden with her
into the house, and nursed her, and tended her
carefully.   And because her account of the wonderful
stone was found correct, all the rest of her story was
believed. So the mother of the Chan and his wife
ruled over the kingdom.

"Henceforth, too, it happened that every month,
on the night of the full moon, the deceased Chan
appeared to his wife, remained with her until
morning dawned, and then vanished into air.   And
the wife recounted this to his mother, but his mother
believed her not, and said, ' This is a mere invention.
If it were true my son would, of a surety, show himself likewise unto me. If I am to believe your
words, you must take care that mother and son
meet one another.'

"When the son of the Chan came on the night
of the full moon, his wife said unto him, ' It is well
that thou comest unto me on the night of every full
moon, but it were yet better if thou camest every
night.' And as she spake thus, with tears in her
eyes, the son of the Chan replied, ' If thou hadst
sufficient spirit to dare its accomplishment, thou
mightest do what would bring me every night; but
thou art young and cannot do it.' ' Then,' said she,

'if thou wilt but come every night, I will do all that is required of me, although I should thereby lose both flesh and bone.'

"Thereupon the son of the Chan spake as follows : 'Then betake thyself on the night of the full moon a berren from this place to the iron old man, and give unto him arrack. A little further you will come unto two rams, to them you must offer batschimak cakes. A little further on you will perceive a host of men in coats of mail and other armour, and there you must share out meat and cakes. From thence you must proceed to a large black building, stained with blood; the skin of a man floats over it instead of a flag. Two aerliks (fiends) stand at the entrance. Present unto them both offerings of blood. Within the mansion thou wilt discover nine fearful exorcists, and nine hearts upon a throne. "Take me! take me!" will the eight old hearts exclaim ; and the ninth heart will cry out, "Do not take me!" But leave the old hearts and take the fresh one, and run home with it without looking round.'

"Much as the maiden was alarmed at the task which she had been enjoined to perform, she set forth on the night of the next full moon, divided the offerings, and entered the house. 'Take me not!' exclaimed the fresh heart; but the maiden seized the fresh heart and fled with it. The exorcists fled after her, and cried out to those who were watching, 'Stop the thief of the heart!' And the two aerlic (fiends) cried, 'We have received offerings of blood!' Then each of the armed men cried out, 'Stop the thief!' But the rams said, 'We have received batschimak cakes.' Then they called out to the iron old man, 'Stop the thief with the heart!' But the old man said, 'I have received arrack from her, and shall not stop her.'

"Thereupon the maiden journeyed on without fear until she reached home; and she found upon entering the house the Chan's son, attired in festive garments. And the Chan's son drew nigh, and threw his arms about the neck of the maiden."

"The maiden behaved well indeed!" exclaimed the Son of the Chan.

"Ruler of Destiny, thou hast spoken words! Ssarwala missdood jakzang." Thus spake Ssidi, and burst from the sack through the air.

Thus Ssidi's ninth relation treats of the Stealing of the Heart.

THE MAN AND HIS WIFE.

When Ssidi had been captured as before, and was being carried away in the sack, he inquired, as he had always done, as to telling a tale; but the Son of the Chan shook his head without speaking a word. Whereupon Ssidi began the following relation :—

"Many, many years since, there lived in the
kingdom of Olmilsong two brothers, and they were
both married. Now the elder brother and his wife
were niggardly and envious, while the younger
brother was of quite a different disposition.

"Once upon a time the elder brother, who had
contrived to gather together abundance of riches,
gave a great feast, and invited many people to
partake of it. When this was known, the younger
thought to himself, 'Although my elder brother has
hitherto not treated me very well, yet he will now,
no doubt, since he has invited so many people to his
feast, invite also me and my wife.' This he certainly
expected, but yet he was not invited. 'Probably,'
thought he, 'my brother will summon me to-morrow
morning to the brandy-drinking.' Because, however, he was not even invited unto that, he grieved
very sore, and said unto himself, 'This night, when
my brother's wife has drunk the brandy, I will go
unto the house and steal somewhat.'

"When, however, he had glided into the treasure-
chamber of his brother, there lay the wife of his
brother near her husband; but presently she arose
and went into the kitchen, and cooked meat and
sweet food, and went out of the door with it. The
concealed one did not venture at this moment to
steal anything, but said unto himself, 'Before I
steal anything, I will just see what all this means.'

"So saying, he went forth and followed the

woman to a mountain where the dead were wont to
be laid.   On the top, upon a green mound, lay a
beautiful ornamental tomb over the body of a dead
man.   This man had formerly been the lover of the
woman.   Even when afar off she called unto the
dead man by name, and when she had come unto
him she threw her arms about his neck; and the
younger brother was nigh unto her, and saw all
that she did.

"The woman next handed the sweet food which
she had prepared to the dead man, and because the
teeth of the corse did not open, she separated them
with a pair of brazen pincers, and pushed the food
into his mouth. Suddenly the pincers bounced back
from the teeth of the dead man, and snapped off the
tip of the woman's nose; while, at the same time,
the teeth of the dead man closed together and bit
off the end of the woman's tongue.   Upon this the
woman took up the dish with the food and went
back to her home.

"The younger brother thereupon followed her
home, and concealed himself in the treasure-chamber, and the wife laid herself down again by her
husband.   Presently the man began to move, when
the wife immediately cried out, 'Woe is me! woe is
me! was there ever such a man?'   And the man
said, 'What is the matter now?'   The wife replied,
'The point of my tongue, and the tip of my nose,
both these thou hast bitten off. What can a woman

do without these two things? To-morrow the Chan shall be made acquainted with this conduct.' Thus spake she, and the younger brother fled from the treasure-chamber without stealing anything.

" On the following morning the woman presented herself before the Chan, and addressed him, saying, 'My husband has this night treated me shamefully. Whatsoever punishment may be awarded to him, I myself will see it inflicted.'

"But the husband persisted in asserting, 'Of all this I know nothing!' Because the complaint of the wife seemed well-founded, and the man could not exculpate himself, the Chan said, 'Because of his evil deeds, let this man be burnt."

"When the younger brother heard what had befallen the elder, he went to see him. And after the younger one had related to him all the affair, he betook himself unto the Chan, saying, 'That the evil-doer may be really discovered, let both the woman and her husband be summoned before you; I will clear up the mystery.'

"When they were both present, the younger brother related the wife's visit to the dead man, and because the Chan would not give credence unto his story, he said : 'In the mouth of the dead man you will find the end of the woman's tongue ; and the blood-soiled tip of her nose you will find in the pincers of brass. Send thither, and see if it be not so.'

"Thus spake he, and people were sent to the place, and confirmed all that he had asserted. Upon this the Chan said, 'Since the matter stands thus, let the woman be placed upon the pile of fagots and consumed with fire.' And the woman was placed upon the pile of fagots and consumed with fire."

"That served her right!" said the Son of the Chan.

"Ruler of Destiny, thou hast spoken words! Ssarwala missdood jakzang!" Thus spake Ssidi, and burst from the sack through the air.

Thus Ssidi's tenth relation treats of the Man and his Wife.

OF THE MAIDEN SSUWARANDARI.

When the Son of the Chan was carrying off Ssidi, as formerly, Ssidi related the following tale :—

"A long while ago, there was in the very centre of a certain kingdom an old pagoda, in which stood the image of Choschim Bodissadoh (a Mongolian idol), formed of clay. Near unto this pagoda stood a small house, in which a beautiful maiden resided with her aged parents. But at the mouth of the river, which ran thereby, dwelt a poor man, who maintained himself by selling fruit, which he carried in an ark upon the river.

"Now it happened once, that as he was returning

home he was benighted in the neighbourhood of the
pagoda. He listened at the door of the house in
which the two old people dwelt, and heard the old
woman say unto her husband, 'We are both grown
exceedingly old ; could we now but provide for our
daughter, it would be well.'

"'That we have lived so long happily together,'
said the old man, 'we are indebted to the talisman
of our daughter. Let us, however, offer up sacrifice
to Bodissadoh, and inquire of him to what condition
we shall dedicate our daughter—to the spiritual
or to the worldly. To-morrow, at the earliest
dawn, we will therefore lay our offering before the
Burchan.'

"'Now know I what to do,' said the listener ; so
in the night-time he betook himself to the pagoda,
made an opening in the back of the idol, and concealed himself therein. When on the following
morning the two old people and the daughter drew
nigh and made their offering, the father bowed himself to the earth and spake as follows :—

"'Deified Bodissadoh! shall this maiden be devoted to a spiritual or worldly life ? If she is to be
devoted to a worldly life, vouchsafe to point out
now or hereafter, in a dream or vision, to whom we
shall give her to wife.'

"Then he who was concealed in the image exclaimed, 'It is better that thy daughter be devoted
to a worldly life. Therefore, give her to wife to the

first man who presents himself at thy door in the morning.'

"The old people were greatly rejoiced when they heard these words; and they bowed themselves again and again down to the earth, and walked around the idol.

"On the following morning the man stepped out of the idol and knocked at the door of the aged couple. The old woman went out, and when she saw that it was a man, she turned back again, and said to her husband, 'The words of the Burchan are fulfilled; the man has arrived.'

"'Give him entrance!' said the old man. The man came in accordingly, and was welcomed with food and drink; and when they had told him all that the idol had said, he took the maiden with the talisman to wife.

"When he was wandering forth and drew nigh unto his dwelling, he thought unto himself, 'I have with cunning obtained the daughter of the two old people. Now I will place the maiden in the ark, and conceal the ark in the sand.'

"So he concealed the ark, and went and said unto the people, 'Though I have ever acted properly, still it has never availed me yet. I will therefore now seek to obtain liberal gifts through my prayers.' Thus spake he, and after repeating the Zoka-prayers (part of the Calmuc ritual), he obtained food and gifts, and said, 'To-morrow I

will again wander around, repeat the appointed
Zoka-prayers, and seek food again.'

"In the meanwhile it happened that the son of the
Chan and two of his companions, with bows and
arrows in their hands, who were following a tiger,
passed by unnoticed, and arrived at the sand-heap
of the maiden Ssuwarandari. 'Let us shoot at that
heap!' cried they. Thus spake they, and shot
accordingly, and lost their arrows in the sand. As
they were looking after the arrows, they found the
ark, opened it, and drew out the maiden with the
talisman.

"'Who art thou, maiden?' inquired they. 'I
am the daughter of Lu.' The Chan's son said,
'Come with me, and be my wife.' And the maiden
said, 'I cannot go unless another is placed in the
ark instead of me.' So they all said, 'Let us put
in the tiger.' And when the tiger was placed in
the ark, the Chan's son took away with him the
maiden, and the talisman with her.

"In the meanwhile the beggar ended his prayers;
and when he had done so, he thought unto himself,
'If I take the talisman, slay the maiden, and sell
the talisman, of a surety I shall become rich indeed.'
Thus thinking he drew nigh unto the sand-heap,
drew forth the ark, carried it home with him, and
said unto his wife, who he thought was within the
ark, 'I shall pass this night in repeating the Zoka-
prayers.' He threw off his upper garment. And

when he had done so, he lifted off the cover of the ark, and said, 'Maiden, be not alarmed?' When he was thus speaking, he beheld the tiger.

"When some persons went into the chamber on the following morning, they found a tiger with his tusks and claws covered with blood, and the body of the beggar torn into pieces.

"And the wife of the Chan gave birth to three sons, and lived in the enjoyment of plenty of all things. But the ministers and the people murmured, and said, 'It was not well of the Chan that he drew forth his wife out of the earth. Although the wife of the Chan has given birth to the sons of the Chan, still she is but a low-born creature.' Thus spoke they, and the wife of the Chan received little joy therefrom. 'I have borne three sons,' said she, 'and yet am noways regarded; I will therefore return home to my parents.'

"She left the palace on the night of the full moon, and reached the neighbourhood of her parents at noontide. Where there had formerly been nothing to be seen she saw a multitude of workmen busily employed, and among them a man having authority, who prepared meat and drink for them. 'Who art thou, maiden?' inquired this man. 'I come far from hence,' replied the wife of the Chan; 'but my parents formerly resided upon this mountain, and I have come hither to seek them.'

"At these words the young man said, 'Thou art

then their daughter?' and he received for answer,
'I am their daughter.'

"'I am their son,' said he. 'I have been told
that I had a sister older than myself. Art thou
she? Sit thee down, partake of this meat and this
drink, and we will then go together unto our
parents.'

"When the wife of the Chan arrived at the
summit of the mountain, she found in the place
where the old pagoda stood a number of splendid
buildings, with golden towers full of bells. And
the hut of her parents was changed into a lordly
mansion. 'All this,' said her brother, 'belongs to
us, since you took your departure. Our parents
lived here in health and peace.'

"In the palace there were horses and mules, and
costly furniture in abundance. The father and
mother were seated on rich pillows of silk, and gave
their daughter welcome, saying, 'Thou art still well
and happy. That thou hast returned home before
we depart from this life is of a surety very good.'

"After various inquiries had been made on both
sides, relative to what had transpired during the
separation of the parties, the old parents said, 'Let
us make these things known unto the Chan and his
ministers.'

"So the Chan and his ministers were loaded with
presents, and three nights afterwards they were
welcomed with meat and drink of the best. But

the Chan said, 'Ye have spoken falsely, the wife of the Chan had no parents.' Now the Chan departed with his retinue, and his wife said, 'I will stop one more night with my parents, and then I will return unto you.'

" On the following morning the wife of the Chan found herself on a hard bed, without pillows or coverlets. 'What is this?' exclaimed she; 'was I not this night with my father and mother—and did I not retire to sleep on a bed of silk?'

" And when she rose up she beheld the ruined hut of her parents. Her father and mother were dead, and their bones mouldered; their heads lay upon a stone. Weeping loudly, she said unto herself, 'I will now look after the pagoda.' But she saw nothing but the ruins of the pagoda and of the Burchan. 'A godly providence,' exclaimed she, ' has resuscitated my parents. Now since the Chan and the ministers will be pacified, I will return home again.'

On her arrival in the kingdom of her husband, the ministers and the people came forth to meet her, and walked around her. 'This wife of the Chan,' cried they, ' is descended from noble parents, has borne noble sons, and is herself welcome, pleasant, and charming.' Thus speaking, they accompanied the wife of the Chan to the palace."

" Her merits must have been great." Thus spake the Son of the Chan.

"Ruler of Destiny, thou hast spoken words! Ssarwala missdood jakzang!' Thus spake Ssidi, and burst from the sack through the air.

Thus Ssidi's eleventh relation treats of the Maiden Ssuwarandari.

THE TWO CATS.

In former days there was an old woman, who lived in a hut more confined than the minds of the ignorant, and more dark than the tombs of misers. Her companion was a cat, from the mirror of whose imagination the appearance of bread had never been reflected, nor had she from friends or strangers ever heard its name. It was enough that she now and then scented a mouse, or observed the print of its feet on the floor; when, blessed by favouring stars or benignant fortune, one fell into her claws—

> "She became like a beggar who discovers a treasure of
>   gold;
> Her cheeks glowed with rapture, and past grief was
>   consumed by present joy."

This feast would last for a week or more ; and while enjoying it she was wont to exclaim—

> "Am I, O God, when I contemplate this, in a dream or
>   awake ?
> Am I to experience such prosperity after such ad-
>   versity ?"

But as the dwelling of the old woman was in general the mansion of famine to this cat, she was

always complaining, and forming extravagant and
fanciful schemes. One day, when reduced to extreme
weakness, she, with much exertion, reached the top
of the hut; when there she observed a cat stalking
on the wall of a neighbour's house, which, like a
fierce tiger, advanced with measured steps, and was
so loaded with flesh that she could hardly raise her
feet. The old woman's friend was amazed to see
one of her own species so fat and sleek, and broke
out into the following exclamation :—

"Your stately strides have brought you here at last; pray
    tell me from whence you come?
    From whence have you arrived with so lovely an appear-
    ance?
    You look as if from the banquet of the Khan of Khatai.
    Where have you acquired such a comeliness? and how
    came you by that glorious strength?"

The other answered, "I am the Sultan's crumb-
eater. Each morning, when they spread the con-
vivial table, I attend at the palace, and there exhibit
my address and courage. From among the rich
meats and wheat-cakes I cull a few choice morsels;
I then retire and pass my time till next day in
delightful indolence."

The old dame's cat requested to know what rich
meat was, and what taste wheat-cakes had? "As for
me," she added, in a melancholy tone, "during my
life I have neither eaten nor seen anything but the
old woman's gruel and the flesh of mice." The
other, smiling, said, "This accounts for the difficulty

I find in distinguishing you from a spider. Your shape and stature is such as must make the whole generation of cats blush; and we must ever feel ashamed while you carry so miserable an appearance abroad.

> You certainly have the ears and tail of a cat,
> But in other respects you are a complete spider.

Were you to see the Sultan's palace, and to smell his delicious viands, most undoubtedly those withered bones would be restored; you would receive new life; you would come from behind the curtain of invisibility into the plane of observation—

> When the perfume of his beloved passes over the tomb of a lover,
> Is it wonderful that his putrid bones should be re-animated?"

The old woman's cat addressed the other in the most supplicating manner: "O my sister!" she exclaimed, "have I not the sacred claims of a neighbour upon you? are we not linked in the ties of kindred? What prevents your giving a proof of friendship, by taking me with you when next you visit the palace? Perhaps from your favour plenty may flow to me, and from your patronage I may attain dignity and honour.

> Withdraw not from the friendship of the honourable;
> Abandon not the support of the elect."

The heart of the Sultan's crumb-eater was melted

by this pathetic address; she promised her new
friend should accompany her on the next visit to
the palace. The latter, overjoyed, went down immediately from the terrace, and communicated every
particular to the old woman, who addressed her
with the following counsel :—

"Be not deceived, my dearest friend, with the
worldly language you have listened to; abandon
not your corner of content, for the cup of the covetous is only to be filled by the dust of the grave,
and the eye of cupidity and hope can only be closed
by the needle of mortality and the thread of fate.

> It is content that makes men rich ;
> Mark this, ye avaricious, who traverse the world :
> He neither knows nor pays adoration to his God
> Who is dissatisfied with his condition and fortune."

But the expected feast had taken such possession
of poor puss's imagination, that the medicinal counsel
of the old woman was thrown away.

> "The good advice of all the world is like wind in a cage,
> Or water in a sieve, when bestowed on the headstrong."

To conclude : next day, accompanied by her companion, the half-starved cat hobbled to the Sultan's
palace. Before this unfortunate wretch came, as it
is decreed that the covetous shall be disappointed,
an extraordinary event had occurred, and, owing to
her evil destiny, the water of disappointment was
poured on the flame of her immature ambition.
The case was this : a whole legion of cats had the

day before surrounded the feast, and made so much
noise that they disturbed the guests; and in consequence the Sultan had ordered that some archers
armed with bows from Tartary should, on this day,
be concealed, and that whatever cat advanced into
the field of valour, covered with the shield of audacity, should, on eating the first morsel, be overtaken
with their arrows. The old dame's puss was not
aware of this order. The moment the flavour of the
viands reached her, she flew like an eagle to the
place of her prey.

Scarcely had the weight of a mouthful been
placed in the scale to balance her hunger, when a
heart-dividing arrow pierced her breast.

> A stream of blood rushed from the wound.
> She fled, in dread of death, after having exclaimed,
> "Should I escape from this terrific archer,
> I will be satisfied with my mouse and the miserable
>   hut of my old mistress.
> My soul rejects the honey if accompanied by the sting.
> Content, with the most frugal fare, is preferable "

LEGEND OF DHURRUMNATH.

DURING the reign of a mighty rajah named Guddeh
Sing, a celebrated, and as it is now supposed, deified
priest, or hutteet, called Dhurrumnath, came, and
in all the characteristic humility of his sect established a primitive and temporary resting-place
within a few miles of the rajah's residence at Runn,
near Mandavie. He was accompanied by his
adopted son, Ghurreeb Nath.

From this spot Dhurrumnath despatched his son
to seek for charitable contributions from the inhabitants of the town. To this end Ghurreeb
Nath made several visits; but being unsuccessful,
and at the same time unwilling that his father
should know of the want of liberality in the city,
he at each visit purchased food out of some limited
funds of his own. At length, his little hoard failing,
on the sixth day he was obliged to confess the
deceit he had practised.

Dhurrumnath, on being acquainted with this,
became extremely vexed, and vowed that from that
day all the rajah's putteen cities should become

desolate and ruined. The tradition goes on to state that in due time these cities were destroyed; Dhurrumnath, accompanied by his son, left the neighbourhood, and proceeded to Denodur. Finding it a desirable place, he determined on performing Tupseeah, or penance, for twelve years, and chose the form of standing on his head.

On commencing to carry out this determination, he dismissed his son, who established his Doonee in the jungles, about twenty miles to the north-west of Bhooj. After Dhurrumnath had remained Tupseeah for twelve years, he was visited by all the angels from heaven, who besought him to rise; to which he replied, that if he did so, the portion of the country on which his sight would first rest would become barren: if villages, they would disappear; if woods or fields, they would equally be destroyed. The angels then told him to turn his head to the north-east, where flowed the sea. Upon this he resumed his natural position, and, turning his head in the direction he was told, opened his eyes, when immediately the sea disappeared, the stately ships became wrecks, and their crews were destroyed, leaving nothing behind but a barren, unbroken desert, known as the Runn.

Dhurrumnath, too pure to remain on the earth, partook of an immediate and glorious immortality, being at once absorbed into the spiritual nature of the creating, the finishing, the indivisible, all-pervading Brum.

This self-imposed penance of Dhurrumnath has shed a halo of sanctity around the hill of Denodur, and was doubtless the occasion of its having been selected as a fitting site for a Jogie establishment, the members of which, it is probable, were originally the attendants on a small temple that had been erected, and which still remains, on the highest point of the hill, on the spot where the holy Dhurrumnath is said to have performed his painful Tupseeah.

THE TRAVELLER'S ADVENTURE.

It is related that a man, mounted upon a camel, in the course of travelling arrived at a place where others from the same caravan had lighted a fire before proceeding on their journey. The fan-like wind, breathing on the embers, had produced a flame; and the sparks, flying over the jungle, the dry wood had become ignited, and the whole plain glowed like a bed of tulips.

In the midst of this was an enormous snake, which, encircled by the flames, possessed no means of escape, and was about to be broiled like a fish, or kabobed like a partridge for the table. Blood oozed from its poison-charged eyes ; and, seeing the man and the camel, it thus supplicated for assistance—

"What if in kindness thou vouchsafe me thy pity ;
Loosen the knot with which my affairs are entangled."

Now the traveller was a good man, and one who feared God. When he heard the complaint of the snake, and saw its pitiable condition, he reasoned thus with himself : "This snake is, indeed, the enemy of man, but being in trouble and perplexity, it would be most commendable in me to drop the seed of compassion, the fruit of which is prosperity in this world, and exaltation in the next." Thus convinced, he fastened one of his saddle-bags to the end of his spear, and extended it to the snake, which, delighted at escape, entered the bag, and was rescued from the flames. The man then opening the mouth of the bag, addressed it thus : "Depart whither thou wilt, but forget not to offer up thanksgiving for thy preservation ; henceforth seek the corner of retirement, and cease to afflict mankind, for they who do so are dishonest in this world and the next—

> Fear God—distress no one ;
> This indeed is true salvation."

The snake replied, "O young man, hold thy peace, for truly I will not depart until I have wounded both thee and this camel."

The man cried out, "But how is this? Have I not rendered thee a benefit? Why, then, is such to be my recompense?

> On my part there was faithfulness,
> Why then this injustice upon thine ?"

The snake said, "True, thou hast shown mercy, but it was to an unworthy object; thou knowest me to be an agent of injury to mankind, consequently, when thou savedst me from destruction,

thou subjectedst thyself to the same rule that
applies to the punishment due for an evil act committed against a worthy object.

"Again, between the snake and man there is a
long-standing enmity, and they who employ fore-
sight hold it as a maxim of wisdom to bruise the
head of an enemy; to thy security my destruction
was necessary, but, in showing mercy, thou hast
forfeited vigilance.   It is now necessary that I
should wound thee, that others may learn by thy
example."

The man cried, "O snake, call but in the
counsel of justice; in what creed is it written, or
what practice declares, that evil should be returned
for good, or that the pleasure of conferring benefits
should be returned by injury and affliction ?"

The snake replied, "Such is the practice amongst
men.   I act according to thy own decree; the same
commodity of retribution I have purchased from
thee I also sell.

Buy for one moment that which thou sell'st for years."

In vain did the traveller entreat, the snake ever
replying, "I do but treat thee after the manner of
men."   This the man denied.   "But," said he, "let
us call witnesses : if thou prove thy assertion, I will
yield to thy will."   The snake, looking round, saw
a cow grazing at a distance, and said, "Come, we
will ask this cow the rights of the question."   When

they came up to the cow, the snake, opening its mouth, said, "O cow, what is the recompense for benefits received ?"

The cow said, "If thou ask me after the manner of men, the return of good is always evil. For instance, I was for a long time in the service of a farmer; yearly I brought forth a calf; I supplied his house with milk and ghee; his sustenance, and the life of his children, depended upon me. When I became old, and no longer produced young, he ceased to shelter me, and thrust me forth to die in a jungle. After finding forage, and roaming at my ease, I grew fat, and my old master, seeing my plump condition, yesterday brought with him a butcher, to whom he has sold me, and to-day is appointed for my slaughter."

The snake said, "Thou hast heard the cow; prepare to die quickly." The man cried, "It is not lawful to decide a case on the evidence of one witness, let us then call another." The snake looked about and saw a tree, leafless and bare, flinging up its wild branches to the sky. "Let us," said it, "appeal to this tree." They proceeded together to the tree; and the snake, opening its mouth, said, "O tree, what is the recompense for good ?"

The tree said, "Amongst men, for benefits are returned evil and injury. I will give you a proof of what I assert. I am a tree which, though growing on one leg in this sad waste, was once flourishing

and green, performing service to every one. When
any of the human race, overcome with heat and
travel, came this way, they rested beneath my shade,
and slept beneath my branches; when the weight of
repose abandoned their eyelids, they cast up their
eyes to me, and said to each other, ' Yon twig would
do well for an arrow ; that branch would serve for
a plough ; and from the trunk of this tree what
beautiful planks might be made! ' If they had an
axe or a saw, they selected my branches, and carried
them away. Thus they to whom I gave ease and
rest rewarded me only with pain and affliction.

> Whilst my care overshadows him in perplexity,
> He meditates only how best to root me up."

"Well," said the snake, "here are two witnesses;
therefore, form thy resolution, for I must wound
thee." The man said, "True; but the love of life
is powerful, and while strength remains, it is difficult
to root the love of it from the heart. Call but one
more witness, and then I pledge myself to submit to
his decree." Now it so wonderfully happened that
a fox, who had been standing by, had heard all the
argument, and now came forward. The snake on
seeing it exclaimed, "Behold this fox, let us ask
it." But before the man could speak the fox
cried out, "Dost thou not know that the recompense
for good is always evil? But what good hast thou
done in behalf of this snake, to render thee worthy

of punishment?" The man related his story. The
fox replied, "Thou seemest an intelligent person,
why then dost thou tell me an untruth?

How can it be proper for him that is wise to speak falsely?
How can it become an intelligent man to state an untruth?"

The snake said, "The man speaks truly, for
behold the bag in which he rescued me." The
fox, putting on the garb of astonishment, said, "How
can I believe this thing? How could a large snake
such as thou be contained in so small a space?"
The snake said, "If thou doubt me, I will again
enter the bag to prove it." The fox said, "Truly if
I saw thee there, I could believe it, and afterwards
settle the dispute between thee and this man." On
this the traveller opened the bag, and the snake,
annoyed at the disbelief of the fox, entered it;
which observing, the fox cried out, "O young
man, when thou hast caught thine enemy, show him
no quarter.

When an enemy is vanquished, and in thy power,
It is the maxim of the wise to show him no mercy."

The traveller took the hint of the fox, fastened
the mouth of the bag, and, dashing it against a
stone, destroyed the snake, and thus saved mankind
from the evil effects of its wicked propensities.

THE SEVEN STAGES OF ROOSTEM.

PERSIA was at peace, and prosperous; but its king, Ky-Kâoos, could never remain at rest. A favourite singer gave him one day an animated account of the beauties of the neighbouring kingdom of Mazenderan : its ever-blooming roses, its melodious nightingales, its verdant plains, its mountains shaded with lofty trees, and adorned to their summits with flowers which perfumed the air, its clear murmuring rivulets, and, above all, its lovely damsels and valiant warriors.

All these were described to the sovereign in such glowing colours that he quite lost his reason, and declared he should never be happy till his power extended over a country so favoured by Nature. It was in vain that his wisest ministers and most attached nobles dissuaded him from so hazardous an enterprise as that of invading a region which had, besides other defenders, a number of Deevs, or demons, who, acting under their renowned chief, Deev-e-Seffeed, or the White Demon, had hitherto defeated all enemies.

141

Ky-Kâoos would not listen to his nobles, who in despair sent for old Zâl, the father of Roostem, and prince of Seestan. Zâl came, and used all his efforts, but in vain; the monarch was involved in clouds of pride, and closed a discussion he had with Zâl by exclaiming, "The Creator of the world is my friend; the chief of the Deevs is my prey." This impious boasting satisfied Zâl he could do no good; and he even refused to become regent of Persia in the absence of Ky-Kâoos, but promised to aid with his counsel.

The king departed to anticipated conquest; but the prince of Mazenderan summoned his forces, and, above all, the Deev-e-Seffeed and his band. They came at his call: a great battle ensued, in which the Persians were completely defeated. Ky-Kâoos was made prisoner, and confined in a strong fortress under the guard of a hundred Deevs, commanded by Arjeng, who was instructed to ask the Persian monarch every morning how he liked the roses, nightingales, flowers, trees, verdant meadows, shady mountains, clear streams, beautiful damsels, and valiant warriors of Mazenderan.

The news of this disaster soon spread over Persia, and notwithstanding the disgust of old Zâl at the headstrong folly of his monarch, he was deeply afflicted at the tale of his misfortune and disgrace. He sent for Roostem, to whom he said, "Go, my son, and with thy single arm, and thy good horse,

Reksh, release our sovereign." Roostem instantly obeyed. There were two roads, but he chose the nearest, though it was reported to be by far the most difficult and dangerous.

Fatigued with his first day's journey, Roostem lay down to sleep, having turned Reksh loose to graze in a neighbouring meadow, where he was attacked by a furious lion; but this wonderful horse, after a short contest, struck his antagonist to the ground with a blow from his fore-hoof, and completed the victory by seizing the throat of the royal animal with his teeth. When Roostem awoke, he was surprised and enraged. He desired Reksh never again to attempt, unaided, such an encounter. "Hadst thou been slain," asked he of the intelligent brute, "how should I have accomplished my enterprise?"

At the second stage Roostem had nearly died of thirst, but his prayers to the Almighty were heard. A fawn appeared, as if to be his guide; and following it, he was conducted to a clear fountain, where, after regaling on the flesh of a wild ass, which he had killed with his bow, he lay down to sleep. In the middle of the night a monstrous serpent, seventy yards in length, came out of its hiding-place, and made at the hero, who was awaked by the neighing of Reksh; but the serpent had crept back to its hiding-place, and Roostem, seeing no danger, abused his faithful horse for disturbing his repose. Another

attempt of the serpent was defeated in the same
way; but as the monster had again concealed itself, Roostem lost all patience with Reksh, whom he
threatened to put to death if he again awaked him
by any such unseasonable noises. The faithful
steed, fearing his master's rage, but strong in his
attachment, instead of neighing when the serpent
again made his appearance, sprang upon it, and
commenced a furious contest. Roostem, hearing
the noise, started up and joined in the combat.
The serpent darted at him, but he avoided it, and,
while his noble horse seized their enemy by the
back, the hero cut off its head with his sword.

When the serpent was slain, Roostem contem-
plated its enormous size with amazement, and, with
that piety which always distinguished him, returned
thanks to the Almighty for his miraculous escape.

Next day, as Roostem sat by a fountain, he saw
a beautiful damsel regaling herself with wine. He
approached her, accepted her invitation to partake
of the beverage, and clasped her in his arms as if
she had been an angel. It happened, in the course
of their conversation, that the Persian hero mentioned the name of the great God he adored. At
the sound of that sacred word the fair features and
shape of the female changed, and she became black,
ugly, and deformed. The astonished Roostem
seized her, and after binding her hands, bid her
declare who she was. " I am a sorceress," was the

reply, "and have been employed by the evil spirit
Aharman for thy destruction; but save my life, and
I am powerful to do thee service." "I make no
compact with the devil or his agents," said the
hero, and cut her in twain. He again poured forth
his soul in thanksgiving to God for his deliverance.

On his fourth stage Roostem lost his way. While
wandering about he came to a clear rivulet, on the
banks of which he lay down to take some repose,
having first turned Reksh loose into a field of grain.
A gardener who had charge of it came and awoke
the hero, telling him in an insolent tone that he
would soon suffer for his temerity, as the field in
which his horse was feeding belonged to a pehloovân,
or warrior, called Oulâd. Roostem, always iras-
cible, but particularly so when disturbed in his
slumbers, jumped up, tore off the gardener's ears,
and gave him a blow with his fist that broke his
nose and teeth. "Take these marks of my temper
to your master," he said, "and tell him to come
here, and he shall have a similar welcome."

Oulâd, when informed of what had passed, was
excited to fury, and prepared to assail the Persian
hero, who, expecting him, had put on his armour
and mounted Reksh. His appearance so dismayed
Oulâd that he dared not venture on the combat till
he had summoned his adherents. They all fell
upon Roostem at once; but the base-born caitiffs
were scattered like chaff before the wind; many

were slain, others fled, among whom was their chief. Him Roostem came up with at the fifth stage, and having thrown his noose over him, took him prisoner. Oulâd, in order to save his life, not only gave him full information of the place where his sovereign was confined, and of the strength of the Deev-e-Seffeed, but offered to give the hero every aid in the accomplishment of his perilous enterprise. This offer was accepted, and he proved a most useful auxiliary.

On the sixth day they saw in the distance the city of Mazenderan, near which the Deev-e-Seffeed resided. Two chieftains, with numerous attendants, met them; and one had the audacity to ride up to Roostem, and seize him by the belt. That chief's fury at this insolence was unbounded; he disdained, however, to use his arms against such an enemy, but, seizing the miscreant's head, wrenched it from the body, and hurled it at his companions, who fled in terror and dismay at this terrible proof of the hero's prowess.

Roostem proceeded, after this action, with his guide to the castle where the king was confined. The Deevs who guarded it were asleep, and Ky-Kâoos was found in a solitary cell, chained to the ground. He recognised Roostem, and bursting into tears, pressed his deliverer to his bosom. Roostem immediately began to knock off his chains. The noise occasioned by this awoke the Deevs, whose

leader, Beedâr-Reng, advanced to seize Roostem;
but the appearance and threats of the latter so
overawed him that he consented to purchase his own
safety by the instant release of the Persian king
and all his followers.

After this achievement Roostem proceeded to the
last and greatest of his labours, the attack of the
Deev-e-Seffeed.   Oulâd told him that the Deevs
watched and feasted during the night, but slept
during the heat of the day, hating (according to
our narrator) the sunbeams. Roostem, as he advanced, saw an immense army drawn out; he
thought it better, before he attacked them, to re-
fresh himself by some repose.   Having laid himself
down, he soon fell into a sound sleep, and at daylight he awoke quite refreshed.   As soon as the
sun became warm, he rushed into the camp.   The
heavy blows of his mace soon awoke the surprised
and slumbering guards of the Deev-e-Seffeed; they
collected in myriads, hoping to impede his progress,
but all in vain.   The rout became general, and
none escaped but those who fled from the field of
battle.

When this army was dispersed, Roostem went in
search of the Deev-e-Seffeed, who, ignorant of the
fate of his followers, slumbered in the recess of a
cavern, the entrance to which looked so dark and
gloomy that the Persian hero hesitated whether he
should advance; but the noise of his approach had

roused his enemy, who came forth, clothed in complete armour. His appearance was terrible; but Roostem, recommending his soul to God, struck a desperate blow, which separated the leg of the Deev from his body. This would on common occasions have terminated the contest, but far different was the result on the present. Irritated to madness by the loss of a limb, the monster seized his enemy in his arms, and endeavoured to throw him down. The struggle was for some time doubtful ; but Roostem, collecting all his strength, by a wondrous effort dashed his foe to the ground, and seizing him by one of the horns, unsheathed his dagger and stabbed him to the heart. The Deev-e-Seffeed instantly expired ; and Roostem, on looking round to the entrance of the cavern, from whence the moment before he had seen numberless Deevs issuing to the aid of their lord, perceived they were all dead. Oulâd, who stood at a prudent distance from the scene of combat, now advanced and informed the hero that the lives of all the Deevs depended upon that of their chief. When he was slain, the spell which created and preserved this band was broken, and they all expired.

Roostem found little difficulty after these seven days of toil, of danger, and of glory, in compelling Mazenderan to submit to Persia. The king of the country was slain, and Oulâd was appointed its governor as a reward for his fidelity.

The success of his arms had raised Ky-Kâoos to
the very plenitude of power; not only men, but
Deevs, obeyed his mandates.   The latter he employed in building palaces of crystal, emeralds, and
rubies, till at last they became quite tired of their
toil and abject condition.   They sought, therefore,
to destroy him; and to effect this they consulted
with the devil, who, to forward the object, instructed
a Deev, called Dizjkheem, to go to Ky-Kâoos and
raise in his mind a passion for astronomy, and to
promise him a nearer view of the celestial bodies
than had ever yet been enjoyed by mortal eyes.
The Deev fulfilled his commission with such success
that the king became quite wild with a desire to
attain perfection in this sublime science.   The devil
then instructed Dizjkheem to train some young
vultures to carry a throne upwards; this was done
by placing spears round the throne, on the points of
which pieces of flesh were fixed in view of the vultures, who were fastened at the bottom.   These
voracious birds, in their efforts to reach the meat,
raised the throne.

Though he mounted rapidly for a short time,
the vultures became exhausted, and finding their
efforts to reach the meat hopeless, discontinued
them; this altered the direction and equilibrium of
the machine, and it tossed to and fro.   Ky-Kâoos
would have been cast headlong and killed had he
not clung to it.   The vultures, not being able to

disengage themselves, flew an immense way, and at
last landed the affrighted monarch in one of the
woods of China. Armies marched in every direction
to discover and release the sovereign, who, it was
believed, had again fallen into the hands of Deevs.
He was at last found and restored to his capital.
Roostem, we are told, upbraided his folly, saying—

" Have you managed your affairs so well on earth
    That you must needs try your hand in those of heaven?"

THE MAN WHO NEVER LAUGHED.

THERE was a man, of those possessed of houses and riches, who had wealth and servants and slaves and other possessions; and he departed from the world to receive the mercy of God (whose name be exalted!), leaving a young son. And when the son grew up, he took to eating and drinking, and the hearing of instruments of music and songs, and was liberal and gave gifts, and expended the riches that his father had left to him until all the wealth had gone. He then betook himself to the sale of the male black slaves, and the female slaves, and other possessions, and expended all that he had of his father's wealth and other things, and became so poor that he worked with the labourers. In this state he remained for a period of years. While he was sitting one day beneath a wall, waiting to see who would hire him, lo! a man of comely countenance and apparel drew near to him and saluted him. So the youth said to him, "O uncle, hast thou known me before now?" The man answered him, "I have not known thee, O my son, at all;

but I see the traces of affluence upon thee, though thou art in this condition." The young man replied, "O uncle, what fate and destiny have ordained hath come to pass. But hast thou, O uncle, O comely-faced, any business in which to employ me?" The man said to him, "O my son, I desire to employ thee in an easy business." The youth asked, "And what is it, O uncle?" And the man answered him, "I have with me ten sheykhs in one abode, and we have no one to perform our wants. Thou shalt receive from us, of food and clothing, what will suffice thee, and shalt serve us, and thou shalt receive of us thy portion of benefits and money. Perhaps, also, God will restore to thee thine affluence by our means." The youth therefore replied, "I hear and obey." The sheykh then said to him, "I have a condition to impose upon thee." "And what is thy condition, O uncle?" asked the youth. He answered him, "O my son, it is that thou keep our secret with respect to the things that thou shalt see us do; and when thou seest us weep, that thou ask us not respecting the cause of our weeping." And the young man replied, "Well, O uncle."

So the sheykh said to him, "O my son, come with us, relying on the blessing of God (whose name be exalted!)." And the young man followed the sheykh until the latter conducted him to the bath; after which he sent a man, who brought him a comely garment of linen, and he clad him with it, and went with him to his abode and his associates. And when the young man entered, he found it to be a high mansion, with lofty angles, ample, with chambers facing one another, and saloons; and in each saloon was a fountain of water, and birds were warbling over it, and there were windows overlooking, on every side, a beautiful garden within the mansion. The sheykh conducted him into one of the chambers, and he found it decorated with coloured marbles, and its ceiling ornamented with blue and brilliant gold, and it was spread with carpets of silk; and he found in it ten sheykhs sitting facing one another, wearing the garments of mourning, weeping, and wailing. So the young man wondered at their case, and was about to question the sheykh who had brought him, but he remembered the condition, and therefore withheld his tongue. Then the sheykh committed to the young man a chest containing thirty thousand pieces of gold, saying to him, "O my son, expend upon us out of this chest, and upon thyself, according to what is just, and be thou faithful, and take care of that wherewith I have intrusted thee." And the young man replied, "I hear and obey." He continued to expend upon them for a period of days and nights, after which one of them died; whereupon his companions took him, and washed him and shrouded him, and buried him in a garden behind the mansion. And death

ceased not to take of them one after another, until
there remained only the sheykh who had hired the
young man. So he remained with the young man
in that mansion, and there was not with them a
third; and they remained thus for a period of
years. Then the sheykh fell sick; and when the
young man despaired of his life, he addressed him
with courtesy, and was grieved for him, and said to
him, " O uncle, I have served you, and not failed in
your service one hour for a period of twelve years,
but have acted faithfully to you, and served you
according to my power and ability." The sheykh
replied, "Yes, O my son, thou hast served us until
these sheykhs have been taken unto God (to whom
be ascribed might and glory!), and we must inevitably die." And the young man said, " O my master,
thou art in a state of peril, and I desire of thee that
thou inform me what hath been the cause of your
weeping, and the continuance of your wailing and
your mourning and your sorrow." He replied, " O
my son, thou hast no concern with that, and require
me not to do what I am unable; for I have begged
God (whose name be exalted!) not to afflict any
one with my affliction. Now if thou desire to be
safe from that into which we have fallen, open not
that door," and he pointed to it with his hand, and
cautioned him against it; " and if thou desire that
what hath befallen us should befall thee, open it,
and thou wilt know the cause of that which thou

hast beheld in our conduct; but thou wilt repent,
when repentance will not avail thee." Then the
illness increased upon the sheykh, and he died;
and the young man washed him with his own
hands, and shrouded him, and buried him by his
companions.

He remained in that place, possessing it and all
the treasure ; but notwithstanding this, he was
uneasy, reflecting upon the conduct of the sheykhs.
And while he was meditating one day upon the
words of the sheykh, and his charge to him not to
open the door, it occurred to his mind that he
might look at it. So he went in that direction,
and searched until he saw an elegant door, over
which the spider had woven its webs, and upon it
were four locks of steel. When he beheld it, he
remembered how the sheykh had cautioned him,
and he departed from it. His soul desired him to
open the door, and he restrained it during a period
of seven days ; but on the eighth day his soul over-
came him, and he said, " I must open that door, and
see what will happen to me in consequence; for
nothing will repel what God (whose name be
exalted !) decreeth and predestineth, and no event
will happen but by His will." Accordingly he arose
and opened the door, after he had broken the locks.
And when he had opened the door he saw a narrow
passage, along which he walked for the space of
three hours ; and lo ! he came forth upon the bank

of a great river.   At this the young man wondered.
And he walked along the bank, looking to the right
and left; and behold! a great eagle descended from
the sky, and taking up the young man with its
talons, it flew with him, between heaven and earth,
until it conveyed him to an island in the midst of
the sea.   There it threw him down, and departed
from him.

So the young man was perplexed at his case, not
knowing whither to go; but while he was sitting
one day, lo! the sail of a vessel appeared to him
upon the sea, like the star in the sky; wherefore
the heart of the young man became intent upon the
vessel, in the hope that his escape might be effected
in it.   He continued looking at it until it came
near unto him; and when it arrived, he beheld a
bark of ivory and ebony, the oars of which were
of sandal-wood and aloes-wood, and the whole of it
was encased with plates of brilliant gold.   There
were also in it ten damsels, virgins, like moons.
When the damsels saw him, they landed to him
from the bark, and kissed his hands, saying to him,
"Thou art the king, the bridegroom."   Then there
advanced to him a damsel who was like the shining
sun in the clear sky, having in her hand a kerchief
of silk, in which were a royal robe, and a crown of
gold set with varieties of jacinths.   Having advanced to him, she clad him and crowned him;
after which the damsels carried him in their arms

to the bark, and he found in it varieties of carpets
of silk of divers colours.   They then spread the
sails, and proceeded over the depths of the sea.

"Now when I proceeded with them," says the
young man, " I felt sure that this was a dream, and
knew not whither they were going with me.   And
when they came in sight of the land, I beheld it
filled with troops, the number of which none knew
but God (whose perfection be extolled, and whose
name be exalted!) clad in coats of mail.   They
brought forward to me five marked horses, with
saddles of gold, set with varieties of pearls and
precious stones ; and I took a horse from among
these and mounted it.   The four others proceeded
with me ; and when I mounted, the ensigns and
banners were set up over my head, the drums and
the cymbals were beaten, and the troops disposed
themselves in two divisions, right and left.   I
wavered in opinion as to whether I were asleep
or awake, and ceased not to advance, not believing
in the reality of my stately procession, but imagin-
ing that it was the result of confused dreams, until
we came in sight of a verdant meadow, in which
were palaces and gardens, and trees and rivers and
flowers, and birds proclaiming the perfection of God,
the One, the Omnipotent.   And now there came
forth an army from among those palaces and
gardens, like the torrent when it poureth down,
until it filled the meadow.   When the troops drew

near to me, they hailed, and lo! a king advanced
from among them, riding alone, preceded by some
of his chief officers walking."

The king, on approaching the young man, alighted
from his courser; and the young man, seeing him
do so, alighted also; and they saluted each other
with the most courteous salutation. Then they
mounted their horses again, and the king said to
the young man, "Accompany us; for thou art my
guest." So the young man proceeded with him,
and they conversed together, while the stately trains
in orderly disposition went on before them to the
palace of the king, where they alighted, and all of
them entered, together with the king and the young
man, the young man's hand being in the hand of the
king, who thereupon seated him on the throne of
gold and seated himself beside him. When the
king removed the litham from his face, lo! this
supposed king was a damsel, like the shining sun in
the clear sky, a lady of beauty and loveliness, and
elegance and perfection, and conceit and amorous
dissimulation. The young man beheld vast affluence
and great prosperity, and wondered at the beauty
and loveliness of the damsel. Then the damsel said
to him, "Know, O king, that I am the queen of
this land, and all these troops that thou hast seen,
including every one, whether of cavalry or infantry,
are women. There are not among them any men.
The men among us, in this land, till and sow and

reap, employing themselves in the cultivation of the
land, and the building and repairing of the towns,
and in attending to the affairs of the people, by the
pursuit of every kind of art and trade; but as to the
women, they are the governors and magistrates and
soldiers." And the young man wondered at this
extremely. And while they were thus conversing,
the vizier entered; and lo! she was a grey-haired
old woman, having a numerous retinue, of venerable
and dignified appearance; and the queen said to her,
"Bring to us the Kádee and the witnesses." So
the old woman went for that purpose. And the
queen turned towards the young man, conversing
with him and cheering him, and dispelling his fear
by kind words; and, addressing him courteously, she
said to him, "Art thou content for me to be thy
wife?" And thereupon he arose and kissed the
ground before her; but she forbade him; and he
replied, "O my mistress, I am less than the servants
who serve thee." She then said to him, "Seest
thou not these servants and soldiers and wealth and
treasures and hoards?" He answered her, "Yes."
And she said to him, "All these are at thy disposal;
thou shalt make use of them, and give and bestow
as seemeth fit to thee." Then she pointed to a
closed door, and said to him, "All these things thou
shalt dispose of; but this door thou shalt not open;
for if thou open it, thou wilt repent, when repentance will not avail thee." Her words were not

ended when the vizier, with the Kádee and the
witnesses, entered, and all of them were old women,
with their hair spreading over their shoulders, and
of venerable and dignified appearance. When they
came before the queen, she ordered them to perform the ceremony of the marriage-contract. So
they married her to the young man. And she prepared the banquets and collected the troops ; and
when they had eaten and drunk, the young man
took her as his wife. And he resided with her
seven years, passing the most delightful, comfortable,
and agreeable life.

But he meditated one day upon opening the door,
and said, "Were it not that there are within it
great treasures, better than what I have seen, she
had not prohibited me from opening it." He then
arose and opened the door, and lo ! within it was
the bird that had carried him from the shore of the
great river, and deposited him upon the island.
When the bird beheld him, it said to him, "No
welcome to a face that will never be happy !" So,
when he saw it and heard its words, he fled from it ;
but it followed him and carried him off, and flew
with him between heaven and earth for the space of
an hour, and at length deposited him in the place
from which it had carried him away ; after which it
disappeared. He thereupon sat in that place, and,
returning to his reason, he reflected upon what he
had seen of affluence and glory and honour, and the

riding of the troops before him, and commanding
and forbidding; and he wept and wailed. He
remained upon the shore of the great river, where
that bird had put him, for the space of two months,
wishing that he might return to his wife; but while
he was one night awake, mourning and meditating,
some one spoke (and he heard his voice, but saw
not his person), calling out, "How great were the
delights! Far, far from thee is the return of what
is passed! And how many therefore will be the
sighs!" So when the young man heard it, he
despaired of meeting again that queen, and of the
return to him of the affluence in which he had been
living. He then entered the mansion where the
sheykhs had resided, and knew that they had experienced the like of that which had happened unto
him, and that this was the cause of their weeping
and their mourning; wherefore he excused them.
Grief and anxiety came upon the young man, and
he entered his chamber, and ceased not to weep and
moan, relinquishing food and drink and pleasant
scents and laughter, until he died; and he was
buried by the side of the sheykhs.

THE FOX AND THE WOLF

A FOX and a wolf inhabited the same den, resorting thither together, and thus they remained a long time. But the wolf oppressed the fox; and it so happened that the fox counselled the wolf to assume benignity, and to abandon wickedness, saying to him, "If thou persevere in thine arrogance, probably God will give power over thee to a son of Adam; for he is possessed of stratagems, and artifice, and guile; he captureth the birds from the sky, and the fish from the sea, and cutteth the mountains and transporteth them; and all this he accomplisheth through his stratagems. Betake thyself, therefore, to the practice of equity, and relinquish evil and oppression; for it will be more pleasant to thy taste." The wolf, however, received not his advice; on the contrary, he returned him a rough reply, saying to him, "Thou hast no right to speak on matters of magnitude and importance." He then gave the fox such a blow that he fell down senseless; and when he recovered, he smiled in the wolf's face,

apologising for his shameful words, and recited these
two verses :—

"If I have been faulty in my affection for you, and
   committed a deed of a shameful nature,
I repent of my offence, and your clemency will extend
   to the evildoer who craveth forgiveness."

So the wolf accepted his apology, and ceased from
ill-treating him, but said to him, "Speak not of that
which concerneth thee not, lest thou hear that which
will not please thee." The fox replied, "I hear and
obey. I will abstain from that which pleaseth thee
not ; for the sage hath said, 'Offer not information
on a subject respecting which thou art not questioned ; and reply not to words when thou art not
invited ; leave what concerneth thee not, to attend
to that which *doth* concern thee ; and lavish not
advice upon the evil, for they will recompense thee
for it with evil.'"

When the wolf heard these words of the fox, he
smiled in his face ; but he meditated upon employing
some artifice against him, and said, "I must strive to
effect the destruction of this fox." As to the fox,
however, he bore patiently the injurious conduct of
the wolf, saying within himself, "Verily, insolence
and calumny occasion destruction, and betray one
into perplexity ; for it hath been said, 'He who is
insolent suffereth injury, and he who is ignorant
repenteth, and he who feareth is safe : moderation
is one of the qualities of the noble, and good
manners are the noblest gain.' It is advisable to

behave with dissimulation towards this tyrant, and he will inevitably be overthrown." He then said to the wolf, "Verily the Lord pardoneth and becometh propitious unto His servant when he hath sinned; and I am a weak slave, and have committed a transgression in offering thee advice. Had I foreknown the pain that I have suffered from thy blow, I had known that the elephant could not withstand nor endure it; but I will not complain of the pain of that blow, on account of the happiness that hath resulted unto me from it; for, if it had a severe effect upon me, its result was happiness; and the sage hath said, 'The beating inflicted by the preceptor is at first extremely grievous; but in the end it is sweeter than clarified honey!'" So the wolf said, "I forgive thine offence, and cancel thy fault; but beware of my power, and confess thyself my slave; for thou hast experienced my severity unto him who showeth me hostility." The fox, therefore, prostrated himself before him, saying to him, "May God prolong thy life, and mayest thou not cease to subdue him who opposeth thee!" And he continued to fear the wolf, and to dissemble towards him.

After this the fox went one day to a vineyard, and saw in its wall a breach; but he suspected it, saying unto himself, "There must be some cause for this breach, and it hath been said, 'Whoso seeth a hole in the ground, and doth not shun it, and be

cautious of advancing to it boldly, exposeth himself
to danger and destruction.' It is well known that
some men make a figure of the fox in the vineyard,
and even put before it grapes in plates, in order
that a fox may see it, and advance to it, and fall
into destruction. Verily I regard this breach as a
snare; and it hath been said, 'Caution is the half
of cleverness.' Caution requireth me to examine this
breach, and to see if I can find there anything that
may lead to perdition. Covetousness doth not
induce me to throw myself into destruction." He
then approached it, and, going round about examining it warily, beheld it; and lo ! there was a
deep pit, which the owner of the vineyard had dug
to catch in it the wild beasts that despoiled the
vines; and he observed over it a slight covering.
So he drew back from it, and said, " Praise be to
God that I regarded it with caution ! I hope that
my enemy, the wolf, who hath made my life miserable, may fall into it, so that I alone may enjoy
absolute power over the vineyard, and live in it
securely." Then, shaking his head, and uttering a
loud laugh, he merrily sang these verses—

" Would that I beheld at the present moment in this
    well a wolf,
  Who hath long afflicted my heart, and made me drink
    bitterness perforce !
  Would that my life might be spared, and that the wolf
    might meet his death!
  Then the vineyard would be free from his presence,
    and I should find in it my spoil."

Having finished his song, he hurried away until he came to the wolf, when he said to him, "Verily God hath smoothed for thee the way to the vineyard without fatigue. This hath happened through thy good fortune. Mayest thou enjoy, therefore, that to which God hath granted thee access, in smoothing thy way to that plunder and that abundant sustenance without any difficulty!" So the wolf said to the fox, "What is the proof of that which thou hast declared?" The fox answered, "I went to the vineyard, and found that its owner had died; and I entered the garden, and beheld the fruits shining upon the trees."

So the wolf doubted not the words of the fox, and in his eagerness he arose and went to the breach. His cupidity had deceived him with vain hopes, and the fox stopped and fell down behind him as one dead, applying this verse as a proverb suited to the case—

"Dost thou covet an interview with Leyla? It is covetousness that causeth the loss of men's heads."

When the wolf came to the breach, the fox said to him, "Enter the vineyard; for thou art spared the trouble of breaking down the wall of the garden, and it remaineth for God to complete the benefit." So the wolf walked forward, desiring to enter the vineyard, and when he came to the middle of the covering of the hole, he fell into it; whereupon the fox was violently excited by happiness and joy, his

anxiety and grief ceased, and in merry tones he
sang these verses—

"Fortune hath compassionated my case, and felt pity for
the length of my torment,
And granted me what I desired, and removed that which
I dreaded.
I will, therefore, forgive its offences committed in former
times;
Even the injustice it hath shown in the turning of my
hair grey.
There is no escape for the wolf from utter annihilation;
And the vineyard is for me alone, and I have no stupid
partner."

He then looked into the pit, and beheld the wolf
weeping in his repentance and sorrow for himself,
and the fox wept with him. So the wolf raised his
head towards him, and said, "Is it from thy compassion for me that thou hast wept, O Abu-l-
Hoseyn?" "No," answered the fox, "by him who
cast thee into this pit; but I weep for the length of
thy past life, and in my regret at thy not having
fallen into this pit before the present day. Hadst
thou fallen into it before I met with thee, I had
experienced refreshment and ease. But thou hast
been spared to the expiration of thy decreed term
and known period." The wolf, however, said to
him, "Go, O evildoer, to my mother, and acquaint
her with that which hath happened to me; perhaps
she will contrive some means for my deliverance."
But the fox replied, "The excess of thy covetousness and eager desire has entrapped thee into de-

struction, since thou hast fallen into a pit from which thou wilt never be saved. Knowest thou not, O ignorant wolf, that the author of the proverb saith, 'He who thinks not of results will not be secure from perils?'" "O Abu-l-Hoseyn!" rejoined the wolf, "thou wast wont to manifest an affection for me, and to desire my friendship, and fear the greatness of my power. Be not, then, rancorous towards me for that which I have done unto thee; for he who hath one in his power, and yet forgiveth, will receive a recompense from God, and the poet hath said—

"'Sow good, even on an unworthy soil; for it will not be fruitless wherever it is sown.
Verily, good, though it remained long buried, none will reap but him who sowed it.'"

"O most ignorant of the beasts of prey!" said the fox, "and most stupid of the wild beasts of the regions of the earth, hast thou forgotten thy haughtiness, and insolence, and pride, and thy disregarding the rights of companionship, and thy refusing to be advised by the saying of the poet?—

"'Tyrannise not, if thou hast the power to do so; for the tyrannical is in danger of revenge,
Thine eye will sleep while the oppressed, wakeful, will call down curses on thee, and God's eye sleepeth not.'"

"O Abu-l-Hoseyn!" exclaimed the wolf, "be not angry with me for my former offences, for forgiveness is required of the generous, and kind conduct

is among the best means of enriching one's-self. How
excellent is the saying of the poet—

"'Haste to do good when thou art able ; for at every season
    thou hast not the power.'"

He continued to abase himself to the fox, and
said to him, "Perhaps thou canst find some means
of delivering me from destruction." But the fox
replied, "O artful, guileful, treacherous wolf! hope
not for deliverance ; for this is the recompense of
thy base conduct, and a just retaliation." Then,
shaking his jaws with laughing, he recited these
two verses—

"No longer attempt to beguile me ; for thou wilt not attain
    thy object.
What thou seekest from me is impossible. Thou hast
    sown, and reap, then, vexation."

"O gentle one among the beasts of prey!" resumed the wolf, "thou art in my estimation more
faithful than to leave me in this pit." He then
shed tears, and repeated this couplet—

"O thou whose favours to me have been many, and whose
    gifts have been more than can be numbered !
No misfortune hath ever yet befallen me but I have
    found thee ready to aid me in it."

The fox replied, "O stupid enemy, how art thou
reduced to humility, submissiveness, abjectness, and
obsequiousness, after thy disdain, pride, tyranny,
and haughtiness ! I kept company with thee
through fear of thine oppression, and flattered thee

without a hope of conciliating thy kindness; but
now terror hath affected thee, and punishment
hath overtaken thee." And he recited these two
verses—

"O thou who seekest to beguile! thou hast fallen in thy
    base intention.
  Taste, then, the pain of shameful calamity, and be with
    other wolves cut off."

The wolf still entreated him, saying, "O gentle
one! speak not with the tongue of enmity, nor look
with its eye; but fulfil the covenant of fellowship
with me before the time for discovering a remedy
shall have passed. Arise and procure for me a
rope, and tie one end of it to a tree, and let down
to me its other end, that I may lay hold of it.
Perhaps I may so escape from my present predicament, and I will give thee all the treasures that I
possess." The fox, however, replied, "Thou hast
prolonged a conversation that will not procure thy
liberation. Hope not, therefore, for thy escape
through my means; but reflect upon thy former
wicked conduct, and the perfidy and artifice which
thou thoughtest to employ against me, and how
near thou art to being stoned. Know that thy soul
is about to quit the world, and to perish and depart
from it: then wilt thou be reduced to destruction,
and an evil abode is it to which thou goest!"
"O Abu-l-Hoseyn!" rejoined the wolf, "be ready in
returning to friendship, and be not so rancorous.

Know that he who delivereth a soul from destruction hath saved it alive, and he who saveth a soul alive is as if he had saved the lives of all mankind. Follow not a course of evil, for the wise abhor it; and there is no evil more manifest than my being in this pit, drinking the suffocating pains of death, and looking upon destruction, when thou art able to deliver me from the misery into which I have fallen." But the fox exclaimed, " O thou barbarous, hard-hearted wretch! I compare thee, with respect to the fairness of thy professions and the baseness of thine intention, to the falcon with the partridge." "And what," asked the wolf, " is the story of the falcon and the partridge ? "

The fox answered, "I entered a vineyard one day to eat of its grapes, and while I was there, I beheld a falcon pounce upon a partridge; but when he had captured him, the partridge escaped from him and entered his nest, and concealed himself in it; whereupon the falcon followed him, calling out to him, ' O idiot! I saw thee in the desert hungry, and, feeling compassion for thee, I gathered for thee some grain, and took hold of thee that thou mightest eat; but thou fleddest from me, and I see no reason for thy flight unless it be to mortify. Show thyself, then, and take the grain that I have brought thee and eat it, and may it be light and wholesome to thee.' So when the partridge heard these words of the falcon, he believed him and

came forth to him ; and the falcon stuck his talons
into him, and got possession of him.   The partridge
therefore said to him, 'Is this that of which thou
saidst that thou hadst brought for me from the
desert, and of which thou saidst to me, " Eat it, and
may it be light and wholesome to thee ? "   Thou
hast lied unto me ; and may God make that which
thou eatest of my flesh to be a mortal poison in thy
stomach !'   And when he had eaten it, his feathers
fell off, and his strength failed, and he forthwith
died."

The fox then continued, " Know, O wolf, that he
who diggeth a pit for his brother soon falleth into
it himself ; and thou behavedst with perfidy to me
first."   " Cease," replied the wolf, " from addressing
me with this discourse, and propounding fables, and
mention not unto me my former base actions.   It is
enough for me to be in this miserable state, since I
have fallen into a calamity for which the enemy
would pity me, much more the true friend.   Consider some stratagem by means of which I may save
myself, and so assist me.   If the doing this occasion
thee trouble, thou knowest that the true friend
endureth for his own true friend the severest labour,
and will suffer destruction in obtaining his deliverance ; and it hath been said, 'An affectionate friend
is even better than a brother.'   If thou procure
means for my escape, I will collect for thee such
things as shall be a store for thee against the time

of want, and then I will teach thee extraordinary stratagems by which thou shalt make the plenteous vineyards accessible, and shalt strip the fruitful trees : so be happy and cheerful." But the fox said, laughing as he spoke, "How excellent is that which the learned have said of him who is excessively ignorant like thee !" "And what have the learned said ?" asked the wolf. The fox answered, "The learned have observed that the rude in body and in disposition is far from intelligence, and nigh unto ignorance ; for thine assertion, O perfidious idiot ! that the true friend undergoeth trouble for the deliverance of his own true friend is just as thou hast said ; but acquaint me, with thine ignorance and thy paucity of sense, how I should bear sincere friendship towards thee with thy treachery. Hast thou considered me a true friend unto thee when I am an enemy who rejoiceth in thy misfortune ? These words are more severe than the piercing of arrows, if thou understand. And as to thy saying that thou wilt give me such things as will be a store for me against the time of want, and will teach me stratagems by which I shall obtain access to the plenteous vineyards and strip the fruitful trees—how is it, O guileful traitor ! that thou knowest not a stratagem by means of which to save thyself from destruction ? How far, then, art thou from profiting thyself, and how far am I from receiving thine advice ? If thou know of stratagems,

employ them to save thyself from this predicament
from which I pray God to make thine escape far
distant.   See, then, O idiot! if thou know any
stratagem, and save thyself by its means from
slaughter, before thou lavish instruction upon
another. But thou art like a man whom a disease
attacked, and to whom there came a man suffering
from the same disease to cure him, saying to him,
'Shall I cure thee of thy disease?' The first man,
therefore, said to the other, 'Why hast thou not
begun by curing thyself?' So he left him and went
his way. And thou, O wolf, art in the same case.
Remain, then, in thy place, and endure that which
hath befallen thee."

Now when the wolf heard these words of the fox,
he knew that he had no kindly feeling for him; so
he wept for himself, and said, "I have been careless
of myself; but if God deliver me from this affliction,
I will assuredly repent of my overbearing conduct
unto him that is weaker than I; and I will certainly wear wool, and ascend the mountains, com-
memorating the praises of God (whose name be
exalted!) and fearing His punishment; and I will
separate myself from all the other wild beasts, and
verily I will feed the warriors in defence of the religion and the poor." Then he wept and lamented;
and thereupon the heart of the fox was moved with
tenderness for him. On hearing his humble expressions, and the words which indicated his repenting

of arrogance and pride, he was affected with compassion for him, and, leaping with joy, placed himself at the brink of the pit, and sat upon his hindlegs and hung down his tail into the cavity. Upon this the wolf arose, and stretched forth his paw towards the fox's tail, and pulled him down to him; so the fox was with him in the pit. The wolf then said to him, "O fox of little compassion! wherefore didst thou rejoice in my misfortune? Now thou hast become my companion, and in my power. Thou hast fallen into the pit with me, and punishment hath quickly overtaken thee. The sages have said, 'If any one of you reproach his brother for deriving his nourishment from miserable means, he shall experience the same necessity,' and how excellent is the saying of the poet—

"'When fortune throweth itself heavily upon some, and encampeth by the side of others,
Say to those who rejoice over us, "Awake: the rejoicers over us shall suffer as *we* have done."'

"I must now," he continued, "hasten thy slaughter, before thou beholdest mine." So the fox said within himself, "I have fallen into the snare with this tyrant, and my present case requireth the employment of artifice and frauds. It hath been said that the woman maketh her ornaments for the day of festivity; and, in a proverb, 'I have not reserved thee, O my tear, but for the time of my difficulty!' and if I employ not some stratagem in the affair of

this tyrannical wild beast, I perish inevitably. How
good is the saying of the poet—

> " 'Support thyself by guile; for thou livest in an age
>   whose sons are like the lions of the forest;
> And brandish around the spear of artifice, that the
>   mill of subsistence may revolve;
> And pluck the fruits; or if they be beyond thy reach,
>   then content thyself with herbage.' "

He then said to the wolf, "Hasten not to kill
me, lest thou repent, O courageous wild beast,
endowed with might and excessive fortitude! If
thou delay, and consider what I am about to tell
thee, thou wilt know the desire that I formed; and
if thou hasten to kill me, there will be no profit to
thee in thy doing so, but we shall die here together."
So the wolf said, "O thou wily deceiver! how is it
that thou hopest to effect my safety and thine own,
that thou askest me to give thee a delay? Acquaint
me with the desire that thou formedst." The fox
replied, "As to the desire that I formed, it was
such as requireth thee to recompense me for it well,
since, when I heard thy promises, and thy confession
of thy past conduct, and thy regret at not having
before repented and done good; and when I heard
thy vows to abstain from injurious conduct to thy
companions and others, and to relinquish the eating
of the grapes and all other fruits, and to impose
upon thyself the obligation of humility, and to clip
thy claws and break thy dog-teeth, and to wear

wool and offer sacrifice to God (whose name be
exalted!) if He delivered thee from thy present
state, I was affected with compassion for thee, though
I was before longing for thy destruction. So when
I heard thy profession of repentance, and what thou
vowedst to do if God delivered thee, I felt con-
strained to save thee from thy present predicament.
I therefore hung down my tail that thou mightest
catch hold of it and make thine escape. But thou
wouldst not relinquish thy habit of severity and
violence, nor desire escape and safety for thyself by
gentleness. On the contrary, thou didst pull me
in such a way that I thought my soul had departed,
so I became a companion with thee of the abode of
destruction and death; and nothing will effect the
escape of myself and thee but one plan. If thou
approve of this plan that I have to propose, we shall
both save ourselves; and after that, it will be
incumbent on thee to fulfil that which thou hast
vowed to do, and I will be thy companion." So
the wolf said, "And what is thy proposal that I am
to accept?" The fox answered, "That thou raise
thyself upright; then I will place myself upon thy
head, that I may approach the surface of the earth,
and when I am upon its surface I will go forth and
bring thee something of which to take hold, and
after that thou wilt deliver thyself." But the wolf
replied, "I put no confidence in thy words; for the
sages have said, 'He who confideth when he should

hate is in error'; and it hath been said, 'He who
confideth in the faithless is deceived, and he who
maketh trial of the trier will repent.'   How excellent also is the saying of the poet—

"'Let not your opinion be otherwise than evil; for ill
    opinion is among the strongest of intellectual qualities.
Nothing casteth a man into a place of danger like the
    practice of good, and a fair opinion!'

    "And the saying of another—

"'Always hold an evil opinion, and so be safe.
Whoso liveth vigilantly, his calamities will be few.
Meet the enemy with a smiling and an open face; but
    raise for him an army in the heart to combat him.'

    "And that of another—

"'The most bitter of thine enemies is the nearest whom
    thou trustest in: beware then of men, and associate
    with them wilily.
Thy favourable opinion of fortune is a weakness: think
    evil of it, therefore, and regard it with apprehension!'"

    "Verily," rejoined the fox, "an evil opinion is
not commendable in every case; but a fair opinion
is among the characteristics of excellence, and its
result is escape from terrors.   It is befitting, O wolf,
that thou employ some stratagem for thine escape
from the present predicament; and it will be better
for us both to escape than to die.   Relinquish,
therefore, thine evil opinion and thy malevolence;
for if thou think favourably of me, I shall not fail
to do one of two things; either I shall bring thee
something of which to lay hold, and thou wilt escape
from thy present situation, or I shall act perfidiously

towards thee, and save myself and leave thee; but this is a thing that cannot be, for I am not secured from meeting with some such affliction as that which thou hast met with, and that would be the punishment of perfidy. It hath been said in a proverb, 'Fidelity is good, and perfidy is base.' It is fit, then, that thou trust in me, for I have not been ignorant of misfortunes. Delay not, therefore, to contrive our escape, for the affair is too strait for thee to prolong thy discourse upon it."

The wolf then said, "Verily, notwithstanding my little confidence in thy fidelity, I knew what was in thy heart, that thou desiredst my deliverance when thou wast convinced of my repentance; and I said within myself, 'If he be veracious in that which he asserteth, he hath made amends for his wickedness; and if he be false, he will be recompensed by his Lord.' So now I accept thy proposal to me, and if thou act perfidiously towards me, thy perfidy will be the means of thy destruction." Then the wolf raised himself upright in the pit, and took the fox upon his shoulders, so that his head reached the surface of the ground. The fox thereupon sprang from the wolf's shoulders, and found himself upon the face of the earth, when he fell down senseless. The wolf now said to him, "O my friend! forget not my case, nor delay my deliverance."

The fox, however, uttered a loud laugh, and replied, "O thou deceived! it was nothing but my

jesting with thee and deriding thee that entrapped
me into thy power; for when I heard thy profession
of repentance, joy excited me, and I was moved
with delight, and danced, and my tail hung down
into the pit; so thou didst pull me, and I fell
by thee. Then God (whose name be exalted!)
delivered me from thy hand. Wherefore, then,
should I not aid in thy destruction when thou art
of the associates of the devil? Know that I dreamt
yesterday that I was dancing at thy wedding, and I
related the dream to an interpreter, who said to me,
'Thou wilt fall into a frightful danger, and escape
from it.' So I knew that my falling into thy
power and my escape was the interpretation of my
dream. Thou, too, knowest, O deceived idiot! that
I am thine enemy. How, then, dost thou hope,
with thy little sense and thine ignorance, that I will
deliver thee, when thou hast heard what rude
language I used? And how shall I endeavour to
deliver thee, when the learned have said that by
the death of the sinner are produced ease to mankind and purgation of the earth? Did I not fear
that I should suffer, by fidelity to thee, such
affliction as would be greater than that which may
result from perfidy, I would consider upon means
for thy deliverance." So when the wolf heard the
words of the fox, he bit his paw in repentance. He
then spoke softly to him, but obtained nothing
thereby. With a low voice he said to him, "Verily,

you tribe of foxes are the sweetest of people in
tongue, and the most pleasant in jesting, and this
is jesting in thee; but every time is not convenient
for sport and joking." "O idiot!" replied the fox,
"jesting hath a limit which its employer trans-
gresseth not. Think not that God will give thee
possession of me after He hath delivered me from
thy power." The wolf then said to him, "Thou art
one in whom it is proper to desire my liberation,
on account of the former brotherhood and friendship
that subsisted between us; and if thou deliver me,
I will certainly recompense thee well." But the
fox replied, "The sages have said, 'Take not as thy
brother the ignorant and wicked, for he will
disgrace thee, and not honour thee; and take not as
thy brother the liar, for if good proceed from thee
he will hide it, and if evil proceed from thee he will
publish it!' And the sages have said, 'For everything there is a stratagem, excepting death; and
everything may be rectified excepting the corruption
of the very essence; and everything may be repelled
excepting destiny.' And as to the recompense
which thou assertest that I deserve of thee, I
compare thee, in thy recompensing, to the serpent
fleeing from the Háwee, when a man saw her in a
state of terror, and said to her, 'What is the matter
with thee, O serpent?' She answered, 'I have
fled from the Háwee, for he seeketh me; and if
thou deliver me from him, and conceal me with

thee, I will recompense thee well, and do thee every
kindness.' So the man took her, to obtain the
reward, and eager for the recompense, and put her
into his pocket; and when the Háwee had passed
and gone his way, and what she feared had quitted
her, the man said to her, ' Where is the recompense,
for I have saved thee from that which thou fearedst
and didst dread?' The serpent answered him, 'Tell
me in what member I shall bite thee; for thou
knowest that we exceed not this recompense.' She
then inflicted upon him a bite, from which he died.
And thee, O idiot!" continued the fox, "I compare
to that serpent with that man. Hast thou not
heard the saying of the poet?—

"' Trust not a person in whose heart thou hast made anger
    to dwell, nor think his anger hath ceased.
 Verily, the vipers, though smooth to the touch, show
    graceful motions, and hide mortal poison.' "

" O eloquent and comely-faced animal!" rejoined
the wolf, "be not ignorant of my condition, and of
the fear with which mankind regard me. Thou
knowest that I assault the strong places, and strip
the vines. Do, therefore, what I have commanded
thee, and attend to me as the slave attendeth to his
master." " O ignorant idiot! who seekest what is
vain," exclaimed the fox, "verily I wonder at thy
stupidity, and at the roughness of thy manner, in
thine ordering me to serve thee and to stand before
thee as though I were a slave. But thou shalt soon

see what will befall thee, by the splitting of thy head with stones, and the breaking of thy treacherous dog-teeth."

The fox then stationed himself upon a mound overlooking the vineyard, and cried out incessantly to the people of the vineyard until they perceived him and came quickly to him. He remained steady before them until they drew near unto him, and unto the pit in which was the wolf, and then he fled. So the owners of the vineyard looked into the pit, and when they beheld the wolf in it, they instantly pelted him with heavy stones, and continued throwing stones and pieces of wood upon him, and piercing him with the points of spears, until they killed him, when they departed. Then the fox returned to the pit, and standing over the place of the wolf's slaughter, saw him dead; whereupon he shook his head in the excess of his joy, and recited these verses—

"Fate removed the wolf's soul, and it was snatched
　　away.
Far distant from happiness be his soul that hath
　　perished.
How long hast thou striven, Abos Tirhán, to destroy
　　me !
But now have burning calamities befallen thee.
Thou hast fallen into a pit into which none shall de-
　　scend without finding in it the blasts of death."

After this the fox remained in the vineyard alone, and in security, fearing no mischief.

THE SHEPHERD AND THE JOGIE.

IT is related that during the reign of a king of
Cutch, named Lakeh, a Jogie lived, who was a wise
man, and wonderfully skilled in the preparation of
herbs. For years he had been occupied in search-
ing for a peculiar kind of grass, the roots of which
should be burnt, and a man be thrown into the
flames. The body so burnt would become gold, and
any of the members might be removed without the
body sustaining any loss, as the parts so taken
would always be self-restored.

It so occurred that this Jogie, whilst following a
flock of goats, observed one amongst them eating of
the grass he was so anxious to procure. He immediately rooted it up, and desired the shepherd who
was near to assist him in procuring firewood.
When he had collected the wood and kindled a
flame, into which the grass was thrown, the Jogie,
wishing to render the shepherd the victim of his
avarice, desired him, under some pretence, to make
a few circuits round the fire. The man, however,
suspecting foul play, watched his opportunity, and,

184

seizing the Jogie himself, he threw him into the fire
and left him to be consumed. Next day, on returning to the spot, great was his surprise to behold the
golden figure of a man lying amongst the embers.
He immediately chopped off one of the limbs and
hid it. The next day he returned to take another,
when his astonishment was yet greater to see that a
fresh limb had replaced the one already taken. In
short, the shepherd soon became wealthy, and revealed the secret of his riches to the king, Lakeh,
who, by the same means, accumulated so much gold
that every day he was in the habit of giving one
lac and twenty-five thousand rupees in alms to
fakirs.

THE PERFIDIOUS VIZIER.

A KING of former times had an only son, whom he contracted in marriage to the daughter of another king. But the damsel, who was endowed with great beauty, had a cousin who had sought her in marriage, and had been rejected; wherefore he sent great presents to the vizier of the king just mentioned, requesting him to employ some stratagem by which to destroy his master's son, or to induce him to relinquish the damsel. The vizier consented. Then the father of the damsel sent to the king's son, inviting him to come and introduce himself to his daughter, to take her as his wife; and the father of the young man sent him with the treacherous vizier, attended by a thousand horsemen, and provided with rich presents. When they were proceeding over the desert, the vizier remembered that there was near unto them a spring of water called Ez-zahra, and that whosoever drank of it, if he were a man, became a woman. He therefore ordered the troops to alight near it, and in-

duced the prince to go thither with him. When
they arrived at the spring, the king's son dismounted from his courser, and washed his hands,
and drank; and lo! he became a woman; whereupon he cried out and wept until he fainted. The
vizier asked him what had befallen him, so the
young man informed him; and on hearing his
words, the vizier affected to be grieved for him, and
wept. The king's son then sent the vizier back to
his father to inform him of this event, determining
not to proceed nor to return until his affliction
should be removed from him, or until he should
die.

He remained by the fountain during a period of
three days and nights, neither eating nor drinking,
and on the fourth night there came to him a horseman with a crown upon his head, appearing like one
of the sons of the kings. This horseman said to
him, "Who brought you, O young man, unto this
place?" So the young man told him his story;
and when the horseman heard it, he pitied him, and
said to him, "The vizier of thy father is the person
who hath thrown thee into this calamity; for no
one of mankind knoweth of this spring excepting
one man." Then the horseman ordered him to
mount with him. He therefore mounted; and the
horseman said to him, "Come with me to my
abode: for thou art my guest this night." The
young man replied, "Inform me who thou art before

I go with thee." And the horseman said, "I am
the son of a king of the Jinn, and thou art son
of a king of mankind. And now, be of good heart
and cheerful eye on account of that which shall
dispel thine anxiety and thy grief, for it is unto
me easy."

So the young man proceeded with him from the
commencement of the day, forsaking his troops and
soldiers (whom the vizier had left at their halting-
place), and ceased not to travel on with his con-
ductor until midnight, when the son of the king of
the Jinn said to him, "Knowest thou what space
we have traversed during this period?" The young
man answered him, "I know not." The son of the
king of the Jinn said, "We have traversed a space
of a year's journey to him who travelleth with
diligence." So the young man wondered thereat,
and asked, "How shall I return to my family?"
The other answered, "This is not thine affair. It
is my affair; and when thou shalt have recovered
from thy misfortune, thou shalt return to thy family
in less time than the twinkling of an eye, for to
accomplish that will be to me easy." The young
man, on hearing these words from the Jinnee, almost
flew with excessive delight. He thought that the
event was a result of confused dreams, and said,
"Extolled be the perfection of him who is able to
restore the wretched, and render him prosperous!"
They ceased not to proceed until morning, when

they arrived at a verdant, bright land, with tall trees, and warbling birds, and gardens of surpassing beauty, and fair palaces; and thereupon the son of the king of the Jinn alighted from his courser, commanding the young man also to dismount. He therefore dismounted, and the Jinnee took him by the hand, and they entered one of the palaces, where the young man beheld an exalted king and a sultan of great dignity, and he remained with them that day, eating and drinking, until the approach of night. Then the son of the king of the Jinn arose and mounted with him, and they went forth, and proceeded during the night with diligence until the morning. And lo! they came to a black land, not inhabited, abounding with black rocks and stones, as though it were a part of hell; whereupon the son of the king of men said to the Jinnee, "What is the name of this land?" And he answered, "It is called the Dusky Land, and belongeth to one of the kings of the Jinn, whose name is Zu-l-Jenáheyn. None of the kings can attack him, nor doth any one enter his territory unless by his permission, so stop in thy place while I ask his permission." Accordingly the young man stopped, and the Jinn was absent from him for a while, and then returned to him; and they ceased not to proceed until they came to a spring flowing from black mountains. The Jinnee said to the young man, "Alight." He therefore alighted from his courser, and the Jinnee said to him, "Drink of this spring."

The young prince drank of it, and immediately became again a man, as he was at first, by the power of God (whose name be exalted!), whereat he rejoiced with great joy, not to be exceeded. And he said to the Jinn, " O my brother, what is the name of this spring?" The Jinnee answered, "It is called the Spring of the Women : no woman drinketh of it but she becometh a man ; therefore praise God, and thank Him for thy restoration, and mount thy courser." So the king's son prostrated himself, thanking God (whose name be exalted!). Then he mounted, and they journeyed with diligence during the rest of the day until they had returned to the land of the Jinnee, and the young man passed the night in his abode in the most comfortable manner ; after which they ate and drank until the next night, when the son of the king of the Jinn said to him, "Dost thou desire to return to thy family this night?" The young man answered, "Yes." So the son of the king of the Jinn called one of his father's slaves, whose name was Rájiz, and said to him, "Take this young man hence, and carry him upon thy shoulders, and let not the dawn overtake him before he is with his father-in-law and his wife." The slave replied, "I hear and obey, and with feelings of love and honour will I do it."

Then the slave absented himself for a while, and approached in the form of an 'Efreet. And when the young man saw him his reason fled, and he was stupefied; but the son of the king of the Jinn said to him, "No harm shall befall thee. Mount thy courser. Ascend upon his shoulders." The young man then mounted upon the slave's shoulders, and the son of the king of the Jinn said to him, "Close thine eyes." So he closed his eyes, and the slave flew with him between heaven and earth, and ceased not to fly along with him while the young man was unconscious, and the last third of the night came not before he was on the top of the palace of his father-in-law. Then the 'Efreet said to him, "Alight." He therefore alighted. And the 'Efreet said to him, "Open thine eyes; for this is the palace of thy father-in-law and his daughter." Then he left him and departed. And as soon as the day shone, and the alarm of the young man subsided, he descended from the roof of the palace; and when his father-in-law beheld him, he rose to him and met him, wondering at seeing him descend from the top of the palace, and he said to him, "We see other men come through the doors, but thou comest down from the sky." The young man replied, "What God (whose perfection be extolled, and whose name be exalted!) desired hath happened." And when the sun rose, his father-in-law ordered his vizier to prepare great banquets, and the wedding

was celebrated; the young man remained there two
months, and then departed with his wife to the
city of his father. But as to the cousin of the
damsel, he perished by reason of his jealousy and
envy.